THE
GREAT AMERICAN
TURQUOISE RUSH
1890–1910

THE
GREAT AMERICAN
TURQUOISE RUSH
1890–1910

Philip Chambless and Mike Ryan

SUNSTONE
PRESS

SANTA FE

Cover photo. Original equipment and turquoise from the Cerrillos Tiffany mine.
Studio Seven Productions/Douglas Magnus.

Sunstone books may be purchased for educational, business, or sales promotional use.
For information please write: Special Markets Department, Sunstone Press,
P.O. Box 2321, Santa Fe, New Mexico 87504-2321.

Book and cover design › Vicki Ahl
Body typeface › Minion Pro
Printed on acid-free paper
∞
eBook 978-1-61139-498-6

Library of Congress Cataloging-in-Publication Data

Names: Chambless, Philip, 1948- author. | Ryan, Mike, 1951- author.
Title: The great American turquoise rush : 1890-1910 / by Philip Chambless
   and Mike Ryan.
Description: Santa Fe : Sunstone Press, 2017. | Includes bibliographical
   references.
Identifiers: LCCN 2016046715 (print) | LCCN 2016049077 (ebook) | ISBN
   9781632931658 (softcover : alk. paper) | ISBN 9781632931665 (hardcover :
   alk. paper) | ISBN 9781611394986
Subjects: LCSH: Turquoise mines and mining--United States--History.
Classification: LCC TN997.T87 C49 2017 (print) | LCC TN997.T87 (ebook) | DDC
   338.2/787--dc23
LC record available at https://lccn.loc.gov/2016046715

SUNSTONE PRESS IS COMMITTED TO MINIMIZING OUR ENVIRONMENTAL IMPACT ON THE PLANET. THE PAPER USED IN THIS BOOK IS FROM
RESPONSIBLY MANAGED FORESTS. OUR PRINTER HAS RECEIVED CHAIN OF CUSTODY (COC) CERTIFICATION FROM: THE FOREST STEWARDSHIP
COUNCIL™ (FSC®), PROGRAMME FOR THE ENDORSEMENT OF FOREST CERTIFICATION™ (PEFC™), AND THE SUSTAINABLE FORESTRY INITIATIVE® (SFI®).
THE FSC® COUNCIL IS A NON-PROFIT ORGANIZATION, PROMOTING THE ENVIRONMENTALLY APPROPRIATE, SOCIALLY BENEFICIAL AND
ECONOMICALLY VIABLE MANAGEMENT OF THE WORLD'S FORESTS. FSC® CERTIFICATION IS RECOGNIZED INTERNATIONALLY AS A
RIGOROUS ENVIRONMENTAL AND SOCIAL STANDARD FOR RESPONSIBLE FOREST MANAGEMENT.

WWW.SUNSTONEPRESS.COM
SUNSTONE PRESS / POST OFFICE BOX 2321 / SANTA FE, NM 87504-2321 /USA
(505) 988-4418 / ORDERS ONLY (800) 243-5644 / FAX (505) 988-1025

Dedicated to Henry Marcus and Arthur G. Hughes.
Two high school English teachers who made a difference.

Contents

My friend Philip Chambless, jewelry making colleague and turquoise lover, has been researching and collecting the history of turquoise mining in New Mexico and the southwestern United States since at least the mid-1990s. Determined to write the true and accurate story of these ancient mines in Cerrillos, New Mexico, he proceeded to uncover obscure documents revealing much of the hitherto unknown truth behind the commonly written and repeated fallacies surrounding the secrets and exaggerations of the mining boom in the 1800s and beyond.

Philip, who lives in the rugged outback Indian country between Zuni and Acoma pueblos of New Mexico, not only works much turquoise into his jewelry designs, but also pursues an equal interest in the mining of turquoise. As things tend to go, it started in Cerrillos with a few old claims, and it became somewhat of an obsession both in terms of the working of the claims and the researching of the history behind them. Philip wanted to write the story, but he found he had stumbled onto a great undiscovered mother-lode of information that led him on adventures throughout the west, connecting the dots. Turns out, it's a big story!

As the years passed, Philip was distracted by health issues, including heart attacks, and love affairs. Yet all the while he researched and mined from New Mexico to Nevada and discovered fascinating connections throughout. He continues to work mining claims in obscure and ancient locations such as Hachita, New Mexico and Nevada, where he recovers blue and green stone that he cuts into rare gems for sale at gem shows in Tucson, Arizona and Santa Fe, New Mexico.

Although the book Philip originally intended shifted to the back burner, he became one of the greatest living knowledge-holders of modern American turquoise mining history. This knowledge is enhanced by his years of hands-on experience in both stone cutting and jewelry making with turquoise. Just when it appeared as though his many Bankers Boxes of collected documents might be headed to the tailings dump of obscurity, Philip met Mike Ryan, an avid turquoise collector with a burning curiosity for the backstory. This book is a result of that fortunate meeting and subsequent collaboration.

— Douglas Magnus, Santa Fe, New Mexico, July 2016

Preface

Philip Chambless

$\mathcal{S}$oon after receiving a bachelor's degree in studio art and history from Troy University in Southern Alabama, I hit the road for the romantic American Southwest. It was a move I have never regretted. Soon after arriving in Tucson, fate intervened and I found a job working in the plant department at the Arizona-Sonoran Desert Museum. Being surrounded by the natural history of the Southwest was a dream come true for me, and I was exposed to much knowledge while I was there. My department curator, Don DuCote, whose father had driven trucks taking turquoise-laden muck to the dumps at Bisbee, gave me my first turquoise stone; it would spawn a love affair that has never died. Being surrounded by staff and docents who proudly wore their turquoise led me to the art of lapidary and silversmithing. In 1974 I moved to the Zuni Mountains of New Mexico where I built a log cabin and soon found a part-time job working at the Ice Caves Trading Post south of Grants. It was the Turquoise Boom of the 1970s, and jewelry traders and Native silversmiths were a daily encounter. Turquoise and silver were readily available in New Mexico, and I utilized my time developing my skills.

Years passed and I moved to Santa Fe in the late 1980s to participate in the art jewelry boom that was taking place there. I will always remember the night at El Farol on Canyon Road when my old friend Doug Magnus was celebrating his recent acquisition of the old Tiffany turquoise mines. As happy as I was for him, I was so jealous I could spit! Well, again fate would come into play and an old, terminally ill miner from Cerrillos/Madrid started giving away his Cerrillos mining claims in the Mine Shaft Tavern. One claim he gave to my friend, jazz musician Doug Lawrence, had a problem, and Doug asked me to go to the BLM and find out what was going on. It was a minor issue but while I was there, I asked about the procedures for locating mining claims. I soon learned the process and acquired my first claims in the Cerrillos Hills.

I was born with a severe handicap to being a turquoise miner—I am red-green colorblind. I have a hard time locating the turquoise on the ground and in the rock, but soon found partners to help me. After learning how to locate one turquoise claim, I saw no sense in stopping there, so I utilized my skills as a researcher to find others using obscure 100-year-old accounts and texts. I might have been colorblind but I was a good researcher and acquired information on every historical turquoise mine in the United States. With my growing volume of research material, people started saying I should write a book, and I had already discovered how sparse and incorrect the history was concerning turquoise mining in the final days of the Wild West. This book works through the tangled stories and miscommunication and reveals who was really behind that great but short-lived rush to the turquoise fields at the turn of the nineteenth and twentieth centuries. It was an exciting time, and I hope you enjoy this trip back into the past to discover the story of America's original gemstone.

Bringing this book to reality required the help and support of many people along the way. There was Henry Marcus, my high school English teacher, who instilled within me the love of literature and gave me his personal copy of Thoreau's *Walden*. Homer Milford and Bill Baxter were always there for me with their knowledge of the Cerrillos area; Steve Kostelecky worked on my early drafts; Amanda Clarke helped with inter-library loans at the University of New Mexico; Susan Berry of the Silver City Museum provided information on the Burro Mountains; Donald Sharp always asked with a loving nudge, "How's the book coming?" Countless librarians, county recorders, and individuals provided me with information over the years; and last, but far from least, Mike Ryan came into my life and said "Let's get it done!" and made it happen.

Mike Ryan

Turquoise is a special stone. Other gemstones have their brilliance and beauty, but one fine diamond is very much like another. Turquoise has a personality all its own that varies from region to region, mine to mine. Even within the same mine, a wide range of color, grade, and pattern will emerge. The expression of the rare high-grade turquoise rises to a level uniting the energies of earth and sky.

This book began for me in 2011 when I retired after a 30-year career as a financial planner and investment advisor. Family and career were my priorities until I retired, and then an interest in turquoise, dormant since the 1970s, reawakened. I began to collect turquoise and became an avid student of the different types and the history of the different mines. As my research continued

I was told again and again: "Ask Philip Chambless. He knows more about the old mines than anyone." I met with Philip and we decided to work together using the research, notes, photos, and text he had accumulated in 25 years, which were stored in more than 20 Bankers Boxes. Throughout 2016 this trove of information, along with additional research, was organized and developed into the narrative of *The Great American Turquoise Rush: 1890–1910*. After working on this book, I am probably the second most knowledgeable person regarding all of the old mines. Philip knows twice as much.

Although I had written a technical book on investment management, *Asset Allocation and the Investment Management Process,* and a more metaphysical book, *The Colors of Money,* this project has been unique in that the topic has never been studied in such a manner for all the mining areas of the period. Homer Milford has written extensively about the Cerrillos district, and *Tiffany Blue* by Patricia McCraw presents the extensive letters of James Patrick McNulty regarding his work with the American Turquoise Company, but the complete story had never been written.

Most of the information available on the history of turquoise has focused on specific mines and the miners who worked them. Seldom has the story gone past the 1940s. The complete story of the first turquoise mines of the modern era has not been told in its entirety until now. Knowing about the beginning of turquoise mining in the United States gives a solid foundation for understanding how the story of turquoise unfolded during the twentieth century. With any story, it is always best to start at the beginning.

I would like to thank the following for their help with this project and all things turquoise: my son Devin and his wife Teena for their help in organizing boxes of research notes and scanning countless images; Linda Hines for helping us make the book better; Bill Jones for sharing his research from the San Bernardino County Recorder's office; Douglas B. Sterrett for his passion for turquoise and for taking the pictures; Homer Milford, Doug Magnus, Joan Mathien, Robert Stapp, Bob Brucia, Joe Tanner, Gene Waddell, and Nila Brown for their insights. And, finally, a special thank you to Pamela, my wife of 43 years, for her support and shared love of turquoise.

John resumed his silent stalk through the timber, seeking a deer to replenish the larder at his camp up the canyon. Starting down the side of a shallow canyon, he was struck by the appearance of a low grass-grown mound over which he had stumbled. A spot of color caught his eye. Stooping he picked up a small piece of red pottery, looked at it idly and tossed it aside. Potsherds held no attraction for him. He was about to walk on when he noticed a peculiarly shaped stone at the edge of the heap. It was a perfectly formed stone axe, obviously of Indian workmanship and obviously very, very old. A gleam of interest lighted his eyes as he examined it. "These must be old Indian diggin's," he muttered, "what'd they be diggin for—gold?" Excitement gripped John as he leaned his rifle against a nearby tree and knelt to scrape in the mound with the stone axe. A glint of blue caught his eye. "Turquoise!" he exclaimed as he examined the bit of blue stone.[1]

Native Americans had been mining turquoise for over a thousand years when settlers first identified it in 1857. Much has been written about the alluring blue stone of the American Southwest: its discovery and mining; its value as a collectable, semi-precious gemstone in jewelry; its mystique and the culture surrounding it. The earliest miners left no written record. Instead, their diggings, many from ancient Native American mining sites, formed a legacy that guided the prospectors that followed, including those featured in *The Great American Turquoise Rush: 1890–1910.*

We chose these two decades because they encompass the Euro-American discovery and mining of turquoise in America. The period began with the western expansion of the United States after the Mexican-American War. It was a spirited time rife with eagerness, eccentricity, and expectation that encompassed countless stories of conflict and collaboration, competition and cooperation, success and failure.

The first mining operations began in the early 1880s with a limited market until George F. Kunz, vice-president and head gemologist for Tiffany and Co. and special agent for the *U.S. Geological Survey*, made a sweeping revelation. In the 1892 *USGS Mineral Resources of the U.S. Publications (MRUS)* he declared turquoise mined in the Southwest equal, if not superior, to Persian turquoise, which had been the standard for hundreds of years going back to the eleventh century. This was a startling reversal from his previous assessments that valued southwest turquoise only as a curio or mineral specimen. His pronouncement set into motion a series of events that created a huge market for turquoise mined in the Southwest, and fierce competition among several companies to dominate that market.

Throughout the 1890s these companies jockeyed to establish their brand as the primary turquoise source in New Mexico, Arizona, Colorado, Nevada, and California. By 1910, a host of circumstances, including a shortage of desirable high-grade—non-matrix, sky blue—material, undercapitalization, legal problems, and finally a serious financial depression, led to the collapse of The Great American Turquoise Rush. By the 1920s, with a burgeoning tourist market for Native American turquoise jewelry, mining efforts shifted from New Mexico to Nevada.

During the Victorian era (1837–1901), turquoise was not integral to Native American jewelry. Rather, it was part of a tradition going back to the time of Louis the 13th, when it was prized on a par, or even above, precious gems such as diamonds, emeralds, and rubies. The finest European jewelers, primarily those in Paris, created detailed pieces only royalty and an emerging class of wealthy business elite could afford.

Gold, turquoise, and diamond brooch, mid-nineteenth century. Designed as a ribbon tied as a bow, set with cabochon turquoise and highlighted with rose diamonds.
From the collection of the late antiques collector Michael Wellby.
Used with permission from Sotheby's.

It was this environment that served as the catalyst for young merchants Charles Lewis Tiffany and John P. Young to establish a stationary and dry goods store in lower Manhattan at 259 Broadway on September 21, 1837. The partners' timing was perfect; they entered a market on the verge of a century of exponential growth by American commerce and industry that yielded great fortunes and a demand for luxury items. They responded by introducing gold jewelry in 1848. In 1851, Tiffany and Co. joined forces with renowned silver manufacturer John C. Moore, a move that set the stage for the company's pre-eminence in high-quality silver creations.

The West was exploding with the arrival of the railroad into areas little changed from the Spanish and Mexican period of 1776–1846. Gold discovered at Sutter's Creek in 1848 precipitated a mining boom that extended throughout the West as miners sought their fortunes by extracting gold, silver, copper, lead, and coal to meet the demands of the flourishing industrial economy.

The Homestead Act of 1862 further fueled western migration, and the growing population far from traditional retailers necessitated a new marketing and distribution approach, spawning the mail order business. The U.S. Postal Service permitted catalogs to be classified as knowledge dissemination aids, which allowed them to be mailed at one cent per pound. The advent of Rural Free Delivery in 1896 also contributed to economical catalog distribution. When Tiffany introduced the *Blue Book* in 1845, the company became a leader in mail order marketing. Others followed, including the first Sear's advertising mailer in 1888, which no doubt made the move west more realistic for many.

The period of The Great American Turquoise Rush comprises the largest organized effort to mine, process, and market turquoise in U.S. history. The ensuing struggle for dominance—if not outright control—of the primary sources is not surprising. These efforts—often between close associates in spirited competition—began in New Mexico and expanded into other states. Their struggle for power planted the seeds for the end of The Great American Turquoise Rush and laid the foundation for the next era of southwest turquoise that began in the 1920s.

Turquoise is rare, high-grade is rarer still, and mining it was labor intensive. After 1910, challenging economics dictated that turquoise be mined by small-scale ventures or that it was a by-product of mining for other minerals. Its formation, most often close to the surface, was difficult to predict, and available mine reserves were problematic to calculate. Determining the feasibility of capital investment was virtually impossible to calculate with any degree of confidence because of grade variance in a mine or even within the same pocket or vein. Once the vein or pocket of nuggets was located, the fragile material could be damaged in the extraction process, requiring large amounts of material to be carefully mined and sorted by hand.

The quantity and value of turquoise mined during the Great American Gold Rush, though the largest in U.S. history, was dwarfed by the precious metals that dominated mining exploration the second half of the nineteenth century. The value of gold mined during the California Gold Rush of 1848–1852 was estimated at two billion dollars. The Comstock Lode, the largest silver deposit ever mined, was valued at $305MM during the boom of 1859–1882. The value of the Leadville, Colorado silver boom of 1879–1893 was estimated to be $82MM. In comparison, the total value of all turquoise mined in New Mexico, by far the largest producer during The Great American Turquoise Rush, was between $6MM and $14MM. When we consider that a dollar from the 1890s is worth about $26 today, adjusted for inflation, those were meaningful numbers, but it is easy to understand why miners' primary incentive was the discovery of metals and other minerals with commercial value. For all its rarity and allure, turquoise has only one commercial application—its use in jewelry, which subjects it to the whims of fashion.

Oral tradition often creates its own history. Stories change with the retelling much like what happens in the children's game of "telephone" when a phrase is passed around a circle person to person with the final message having little resemblance to the original. The stories of turquoise have their own blend of fact and fiction. The many Tiffany turquoise mines that exist throughout the Southwest provide an example of this. Although it is certainly true Tiffany and Co. purchased turquoise from various sources and was perhaps the largest single turquoise buyer during The Great American Turquoise Rush, neither Charles Lewis Tiffany nor the company he founded ever owned a turquoise mine, though he probably had a small equity holding in and some debt from one company, the American Turquoise Company (ATC). This exaggeration is easy to understand when considering the advantage any mine owners might have in associating with the most successful brand on the market.

A story from *Lost Treasures and Old Mines,* a compilation of writings from the New Mexico Federal Writers Project—part of the WPA—contains another example of oral tradition. In this example, Ernest Prescott Morey relates a story told to him by Selma Close Roach, a German immigrant living in Silver City, New Mexico. In 1903, Felix Vogel from Germany, Louis Rothschild from England, and Adolphe Armenne from France immigrated to the United States to seek their fortune. They bought turquoise claims in Tyrone, New Mexico from Tom Parker with capital from Rothschild, scion of a famous wealthy family. Armenne was connected with Tiffany and Co. With experience in the jewelry business, Armenne remained in New York to coordinate the business side of the operation, and Vogel was responsible for managing the mine. After several years they had accumulated a good-sized fortune and Vogel went back to Germany. He returned to Tyrone with a bride and their maid, Miss Selma Close, and set himself up in the grocery business to support the still prosperous mines and the workers who lived near the operation. Roach related several humorous and poignant anecdotes to Morey, including the outrage of a competing Silver City grocer when Vogel attempted to introduce margarine to the area. At the end of the story, the turquoise boom ended and in 1911 Vogel went to Mexico to invest in a salt mine.[2]

Indeed a Felix Vogel was the first superintendent of the Azure Mining Company, and Meyer D. Rothschild, a prominent New York jeweler, and Gyulo Armeny, a Hungarian immigrant, New York jeweler, and successful pen manufacturer who put together the claims the company mined northwest of those Thomas Parker accumulated, were investors and officers of the company. Vogel retired as superintendent in 1901, and though he may very well have traveled to Germany and back, we have no record of his movements.

Although oral tradition may provide important clues for an historian, it is critical to distinguish the true story supported by documented evidence. For those chronicling history, deciding what to include and what to leave out during any relevant period is daunting. Our focus here is on the charismatic characters that immortalize our central historical premise, but other stories remain to be told. We hope the research will continue.

Notes

1. Charles L. Knaus, "Sky Stones," *New Mexico Magazine,* March 1948, 23.
2. Ann Lacy and Anne Valley-Fox, eds., *Lost Treasures and Old Mines,* Santa Fe: Sunstone Press, 2011, 183–185.

1

The First American Turquoise Rush

It is said the victors write the history, and this is certainly true of the history of early North America and the United States. All too often a story line is selected, one that fits an established image of a specific culture and society, and then facts are included, or excluded, to support the predetermined narrative. The Great American Turquoise Rush of the 1890s was a result of attempts by corporate interests, primarily funded by east coast capital, to establish economic control over turquoise production in the Southwest. Although these efforts to establish a de facto turquoise cartel to control supply and price were unsuccessful, records show the Ancestral Puebloan culture of what is now referred to as the Chaco Canyon region of New Mexico achieved this.

Long before European colonists named America and long before The Great American Turquoise Rush of the 1890s, an organized system of mining, processing, and distributing turquoise existed on a scale that wasn't equaled again until the nineteenth century. Prior to and after colonization of North America in the sixteenth century, the original inhabitants of the American continents were depicted as savages, lacking the ability to live in a civilized manner as defined by the conquering powers. Nothing could be further from the truth. At a time when Western Europe was wallowing in the misery and ignorance of the Dark Ages that followed the collapse of the Roman Empire, Native cities with populations exceeding those of the major cities of Europe existed in North America, and embraced a governance and infrastructure not seen in the West until the fifteenth century Renaissance. The Mississippian culture, centered on Cahokia in Illinois, built sophisticated cities with a network of trade that extended west to the Pacific Ocean. The Chacoan culture of northwest New Mexico had a highly developed social structure and an extensive trading system with other native peoples over a wide-ranging area.

Indigenous native populations had already worked the deposits in every mining area involved in The Great American Turquoise Rush before the Spanish, the Mexicans, and the Americans arrived. Spanish conquerors that settled in the north of Mexico around the provincial capital of Santa Fe left written records detailing the presence of turquoise and its importance to the native people. During the mid-nineteenth century, prospectors searching for deposits of silver and gold discovered old mining sites. More recently, archeological digs at sites like Pueblo Bonito in Chaco Canyon uncovered 60,000 examples of items of or adorned with turquoise, and ongoing research at these sites supports the developing theories of the existence of a complex turquoise trading network.

Turquoise and Conquest

> *"I and my companions suffer from a disease of the heart which can only be cured with gold." —Hernán Cortés*[1]

When Cortés' conquest of Mexico began in 1519, he was vastly outnumbered by the native populations but he had several key advantages. First was the superior technology of the Spaniards. Indians fighting on foot with obsidian-edged weapons were no match for armored warriors with edges of steel mounted on horses. Secondly the Aztec had brutally suppressed their vassal state neighbors who were now eager to support the Spaniards. Montezuma also made a fatal error in believing that Cortés was the second coming of their god Quetzalcoatl. Perhaps most important was the transmission of epidemic diseases for which the native people had no natural immunity.

Montezuma presented Cortés with gifts of turquoise with little value to the Europeans but of the highest significance to the Aztecs, including a mask of Quetzalcoatl made of turquoise and other turquoise mosaic items. Turquoise in pre-Columbian Mesoamerica carried a value far beyond the concept of wealth known to the Europeans. It was a metaphor for life, central to their social and religious structure. According to archaeologists Garman Harbottle and Phil C. Weigand, this mask (Figure 2) was probably the one presented to Cortés by Montezuma. Although no record has been found of turquoise being among the first items Cortés shipped to Charles V, such artifacts were certainly included in subsequent shipments and several are represented in the collections of the British Museum.[2] This marked the first encounter European colonists had with turquoise in America. Although the native peoples valued it above all other gems and minerals, the Spaniards had little desire for the stone and were far more interested in silver and gold.

Mosaic mask of Quetzalcoatl.
(figure 2) © The Trustees of the British Museum

Mask, (figure 3) human face, possibly representing Xiuhtecuhtli.
© The Trustees of the British Museum

The mask shown in Figure 3 represents a human face, possibly Xiuhtecuhtli. It is made of cedar wood *(Cedrela odorata)* and covered in turquoise mosaic with scattered turquoise cabochons. The pierced elliptical eyes are fashioned of mother-of-pearl *(Pinctada mazatlantica)* and the teeth are made of conch *(Strombus)* shell (although two are modern synthetic replacements). The eyelids are gilded, the interior surface of the mask painted with cinnabar, and the wood carved to produce a curve for underlying contours of the face.[3]

No significant turquoise deposits had been uncovered in the immediate area of central Mexico, and when the Spaniards asked the natives about the source of these stones they referenced "to the north." Although it was long thought Mesoamerican tribes and those of the Southwest had little direct contact, recent studies have demonstrated a highly developed formal trading system did exist, and turquoise was a central element in that trade.[4]

Prior to the mid nineteenth century, the only historical records regarding turquoise in North America came from Spanish chroniclers that detailed the conquest of Mexico and the Spanish entrada into New Mexico. Although these provide anecdotal accounts of turquoise ornaments the native people prized and wore, they offer little insight into how or where the turquoise was mined and how it was distributed. The Spanish conquerors were far more interested in locating the deposits of silver and gold.

In the 1800s, people thought the ancient turquoise mines were Mesoamerican gold and turquoise workings because they didn't think the local natives were capable of that level of sophistication. This is evident with mine names such as Aztec, Toltec, and Montezuma, to name a few. Recent scientific studies now verify that an extensive trading network existed between Mesoamerica and the American Southwest.[5] It has been reported that from as early as A.D. 350–800, turquoise from the Cerrillos area of modern New Mexico traveled by trading exchanges between the Hohokam and Mogollon and Sonoran people. The Hohokam traded shells for turquoise, and in turn traded turquoise for pyrite mirrors, copper bells, and more exotic items like scarlet macaws. The item exchange facilitated cultural diversity, and most likely influenced the development of subsequent Pueblo, Zuni, Hopi, Navajo, and Apache societies.[6]

The Chaco Phenomenon

The very first turquoise rush in America began in the tenth century and continued into the thirteenth. It was created by networks of villages that were part of regional systems. They were complex societies of urban sedentary farmers who had the means and ability to travel and trade in a wide area[7] extending over what is now New Mexico and centered in the San Juan River basin of the Four Corners area and the Gila and Salt River basins of Arizona.

Centuries later, a new race of people entered the land once held by the Ancestral Puebloan, or Anasazi, a Navajo name meaning "ancestors of our enemies." These Quakers were hearty settlers whose faith supported rather than hindered their ability to face hardship. They ventured from Utah into the Mancos Valley near Durango, Colorado. Lured by the promise of mineral wealth, they soon learned that farming and ranching were more stable ways to eke out a living than prospecting in an often unforgiving land. In 1880 B.K. Wetherill established the Alamo Ranch. His sons, John and Richard, later played a major role in the early development of archeology in the American Southwest and our understanding of the Ancestral Puebloans.

In the winter of 1888, while searching for wayward cattle in the canyons of Mesa Verde, Richard Wetherill and his brother-in-law Charlie Mason became the first Euro-Americans to see the magnificent ancient cliff dwellings of Mesa Verde. They collected several samples from the ruins, which they sent to the Smithsonian for purchase. The museum claimed lack of funds, and then lost the entire first shipment, after which the Denver Historical Society stepped in and purchased other artifacts. Private collectors purchased other samples in 1892 and placed them on exhibit at the 1893 World Colombian Exposition in Chicago before donating them to the University of Pennsylvania.

Traders John and Richard Wetherill became well known to the Navajo. Richard's trading post was in Pueblo Bonito in Chaco Canyon, New Mexico and John's was in Kayenta, Arizona. Both were considered excellent guides who knew the land and its peoples. Richard led the first team of archaeologists to the ruins of Pueblo Bonito in 1896. These cowboy archaeologists were criticized for their often unprofessional methods, yet without their early efforts, the ruins at Mesa Verde and Pueblo Bonito most likely would have received much harsher treatment at the hands of less ethical scavengers.

Excavations at Pueblo Bonito revealed it to be the largest of the ancient Great House ruins in Chaco Canyon and a major significant cultural, economic, and religious center. To date, over 65,000 turquoise artifacts such as the beads shown here have been recovered along with thousands of additional items.

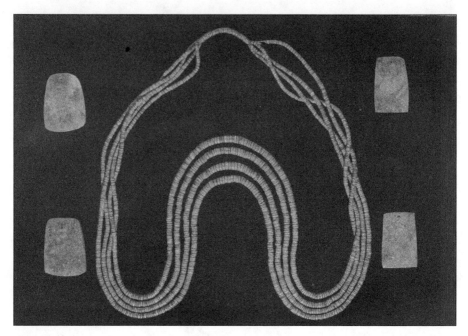

Turquoise beads. Pueblo Bonito. National Geographic, September 1925.
Photo Charles Martin

Although the source of Chaco turquoise has often been assigned to the mines in the Cerrillos Mining District near Santa Fe, New Mexico, many other areas were explored by Native American people. Since William P. Blake's exploration of Mount Chalchihuitl at Cerrillos in 1857, many additional sites of American Indian turquoise mining activity have been discovered, often by prospectors searching for other minerals. In the 1870s and 1880s, Indian turquoise mines were discovered in areas of New Mexico, Arizona, Nevada, Colorado, and the Mojave Desert area of California, all exhibiting similar mining technology and methods. In a paper presented to the Arizona Archeological Association in December 1898, Blake describes evidence of native mining activity in Mohave County, Arizona near Kingman, and Cochise County near Tombstone, and the well-known mines in the Burro Mountains and Cerrillos areas of New Mexico. Referencing the historical records of early Spanish Conquistadors who had noted the high esteem Aztecs held for the gemstone, Blake speculated:

"The wide geographical distribution of the sources of the gem, and the fact that all localities found by us have been anciently worked, indicate the universal desire to obtain it. These facts appear to me to be good evidence of the substantial unity of the races which formerly held sway from the Navajo and Zuni country to the capitals of the Montezumas."[8]

Although it has long been suspected that an extensive turquoise trade existed between Mesoamerica and the American Southwest, scientific proof has only recently been able to support these theories. Building upon the research of Mathien[9], Harbottle and Wiegand[10], and others, new advances in research techniques have demonstrated that the turquoise artifacts in and around Pueblo Bonito originated not only from the Cerrillos area, but also from areas of present-day California, Colorado, Nevada, and Arizona.[11]

A database of 22 turquoise resource areas in the United States and northern Mexico has been compiled using the capabilities of isotope ratios of hydrogen and copper. When turquoise samples from Pueblo Bonito were compared to this database, it was discovered that of 29 artifacts sampled, 13 were linked to turquoise deposits at Cerrillos and the Jarilla Mountains of New Mexico and Villa Grove, Colorado, plus four others were linked to Crescent Peak and Lone Mountain in Nevada. Comparisons from additional sites have linked artifacts to turquoise mined from the Royston District in Nevada and the Mojave Desert region of California. Research is in its early stages. When additional samples are integrated into the database, further evidence is expected to support the existence of an extensive turquoise trading network between the peoples of Mesoamerica, A.D. 800–1100, and later within the American Southwest, A.D. 1100–1300.

Throughout *The Great American Turquoise Rush: 1890–1910*, we will show how this period was the largest concerted effort to mine and distribute turquoise in history. As research continues on the early miners, we may have to reappraise our opinion as prehistoric periods are redefined and become truly historic. These earliest turquoise explorers deserve recognition. They were motivated solely out of awe and adoration of what they considered a magical stone that united the sky and the earth. With only rock and fire, they extracted the stone at great physical cost and developed a sophisticated and far-reaching trade network. Without their efforts, this story would never be told.

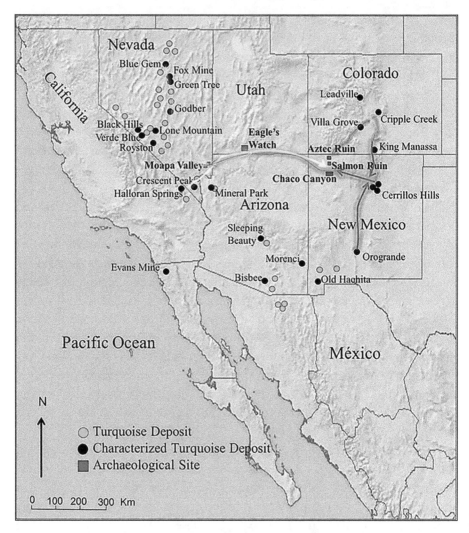

Turquoise map of early mines. Those in black are sites of early turquoise mining that have been sampled and geologically tested. Those in blue are known turquoise deposits both from prehistoric and modern period that have not been tested. The colored lines indicate trading patterns of the early period. Map by Sharon Hull from Elsevier with permission.

**Pueblo Indian with hand drill.
Bureau of Ethnology Annual
Report, 1882. Public domain.**

Notes

1. W.B. Carter, *Indian Alliances and the Spanish in the Southwest, 750–1750,* 85.
2. C. McEwan, A. Middleton, C. Cartwright, R. Stacey, *Turquoise Mosaics from Mexico,* Duke University Press, 2006, 13.
3. Ibid. The name "Xiuhtecuhtli" also means "Turquoise Lord," and this lord is shown in the codices adorned with turquoise. This mask dates from 1400–1521.
4. G. Harbottle and P.C. Weigand, "Turquoise in Pre-Columbian America." *Scientific American,* February 1992, 78.
5. P.C. Weigand, "The Macroeconomic Role of Turquoise within the Chaco Canyon System." In *Anasazi Regional Organization and the Chaco System,* D.E. Doyel, ed., Maxwell Museum of Anthropology, Anthropological Papers no. 5, Albuquerque: University of New Mexico, 169-183.
6. W.B. Carter, *Indian Alliances and the Spanish in the Southwest, 750–1750,* 27–28.
7. Ibid., 43.
8. W.P. Blake, *Aboriginal Turquoise Mining in Arizona and New Mexico.* Read before the Arizona Archeological Association, December 1898.

9. F.J. Mathien, *Economic Exchange Systems in the San Juan Basin.* Unpublished PhD dissertation, Department of Anthropology, University of New Mexico, Albuquerque, 1983. The Mobile Trader and the Chacoan Anasazi. In Proceedings of the Anasazi Symposium, 1981, compiled and edited by J.E. Smith, pp. 196-206. Mesa Verde Museum Association, Inc.

10. P.C. Weigand and G. Harbottle, "The Role of Turquoises in the Ancient Mesoamerican Trade Structure," In *The American Southwest and Mesoamerica: Systems of Prehistoric Exchange,* J.E. Ericson and T.G. Baugh, eds., (New York and London: Plenum Press, Pub date), 159-177.

11. S. Hull, M. Fayek, F.E. Mathien, H. Roberts, "Turquoise Trade of the Ancestral Puebloan: Chaco and Beyond." *Journal of Archaelogical Science* 45(2014), 187–195.

New Mexico

2

Cerrillos

William Phipps Blake and Discovery

Following the Mexican War, the United States and Mexico signed the Treaty of Guadalupe Hidalgo in 1848. The treaty gave the United States undisputed control of Texas, established the U.S.-Mexican border of the Rio Grande, and ceded to the United States the area that comprises California, Nevada, Arizona, Utah, and New Mexico.

With the discovery of gold at Sutter's Creek in 1849, the opening of the West became a central policy objective for the United States. Political maneuvering intensified as efforts increased to determine how the anticipated wealth and economic opportunity could benefit the respective interests of both North and South. In 1853, Congress authorized $150,000 for the survey of potential rail routes. The surveys covered different areas: The Northern Pacific covered St. Paul, Minnesota to Puget Sound. The Central Pacific ran between St. Louis and San Francisco; two Southern Pacific surveys covered Oklahoma to Los Angeles, a route similar to the western part of the later Santa Fe Railroad, and then Route 66, which became Interstate 40; and the southernmost went across Texas to San Diego. Although Congress chose the War Department to oversee survey management in the belief it would be a neutral administrator, Jefferson Davis, Secretary of War, was anything but a neutral observer when it came to putting forth the interests of the southern states.

Davis was intrigued with the idea of using camels to replace Army mules for military transport in the Southwest. In an appeal to romantic military imagery, he extolled Napoleon's use of camels during the Egypt campaign, comparing Arab nomads to hostile American Indians.[1] In 1855, he obtained $30,000 from Congress for the purpose of funding the Wagon Road Program led by former California Secretary of Indian Affairs Edward F. Beale. Beale had served in the Navy and was personal secretary to Robert F. Stockton, who headed U.S. forces in California during the Mexican War. He was assigned to join General Stephen W. Kearney's land forces that, following the successful conquest of New Mexico, were moving overland to join Stockton's navel squadron. On December 6, 1846 he reached Kearney shortly before the Battle of San Pasqual, 30 miles from San Diego. Kearney's forces suffered severe causalities at the hands of well-trained California mounted lancers that surrounded them and cut them off from Stockton. Beale, with Kit Carson and a Delaware scout, broke through the enemy lines to reach Stockton, who sent troops in support of the beleaguered Kearney.

The dramatic story of the troops' passage, bootless and with no food or water, furthered the reputation of Carson and made Beale a recognized name. Following procurement of 50 or so hearty camels, the expedition set out from San Antonio on June 25, 1857, proceeding to El Paso, and then following the Rio Grande north to Albuquerque. The objective was to survey a formal wagon route from Fort Defiance, Arizona west to the Colorado River and on to California. The group traveled through the mountains to finish their journey in the fall at Beale's Tejon ranch near Bakersfield, California.

Although the camel corps has been largely forgotten, its legacy lives on in historical accounts. The wagon route from Albuquerque, though not chosen for the Transcontinental Railroad route, was selected for the Santa Fe Railroad 20 years later, and travelers on Interstate 40, fondly remembering old Route 66, follow the path pioneered by Beale and his camels.

William Phipps Blake, born in New York City on June 1, 1826, received his PhD from Yale's Sheffield Scientific School in 1852. From 1853 to 1856 he served as official government geologist and mineralogist for the Pacific Railroad Survey in the far West. Upon completion of this work in 1856, Blake took a position as a geologist with the government Wagon Road Program. An illness prevented him from continuing with the expedition beyond Albuquerque, but he used his remaining time in New Mexico to conduct several local geological investigations.

In August of 1857, he traveled to Santa Fe where Navajos at the Plaza told Blake about a highly valued green gemstone called "Chalchihuitl" they often used in their personal adornments, and he set out to locate its origin. Chalchihuitl was an Aztec word denoting both turquoise and jade, which the Pueblo tribes had adopted. Believing the gemstone could be turquoise, Blake's investigations into the Chalchihuitl rumors led him to a small hill located in the midst of a small mountainous area just 20 miles south of Santa Fe.

On reaching the location, he was astonished at the extent of the excavations that had been undertaken using only Stone Age tools and fire. The immense pit measured about 200 feet deep and more than 300 feet wide. One-hundred-year-old pine trees and lichen-covered rocks in the dumps gave testimony of its antiquity.[2]

At the time of Blake's visit, the only activity he saw was natives living in the recesses of the cliff face that worked the ancient dumps in groups of two or three, breaking out the gem material from rock extracted centuries before. A mineral analysis performed later at the Yale Analytical Laboratory proved the material to be nearly identical in composition to turquoise.

Blake was one of the most influential geologists of the late nineteenth century. His contribution regarding the early discovery of turquoise by the Ancestral Puebloans and the more recent mining by local Pueblo Indians, although just a small portion of the scope of his study, provided the foundation for later mining efforts, and sparked the interest of investors in New York and Chicago.

William Phipps Blake. University of Arizona Main Library Special Collections.

Blake sketches of Mount Chalchihuitl 1857. Arizona Historical Society, MS78v38 Illustrations A and B. At the time of Blake's first visit in 1857 field photography was in its infancy and cartographers and geologists relied on sketches and drawings for recording images.

In January of 1598, Juan Onate left from a small mining town on the northern frontier with 129 colonists to continue the entrada into New Mexico that Coronado had begun between 1539 and 1542. Onate established a capital near the confluence of the Rio Grande and Chama Rivers at the Tewa pueblo, Ohke, which was renamed San Juan de los Caballeros. (The San Juan Pueblo returned to its former name, Ohkay Owinghe, in November 2005.) The nearby pueblo of Yunque was also settled and renamed San Gabriel. In 1608, the colony moved 25 miles south, where Santa Fe was founded and remained the only organized municipality in New Mexico until 1695 when Santa Cruz, Bernalillo, and the mining camp of Real de Cerrillos were established. Albuquerque was not founded until 1705.

In September, Onate called a gathering in San Juan of the surrounding pueblos where the natives were told the conquerors had come to live peacefully, govern justly, teach them the word of God, and protect them from their enemies. At this time, as shown from tree ring analysis, the area was in the last years of the driest decade in a thousand years. This had undoubtedly placed extreme hardship on inhabitants, leading to shortages and conflict, and they most likely welcomed the prospect of protection from these powerful newcomers.

The promised peace was short-lived. In December, the nephew of Onate and 10 other soldiers were killed near Acoma Pueblo in response to the rape of an Acoma woman. In retaliation, Onate rejected his principles of pacification and decided to make an example of the Acoma people. After intense fighting resulting in the death of 500 men and 300 women and children, the pueblo surrendered. The conquistadors chopped one foot off every male survivor over the age of 25, and every other native was sentenced to 20 years (a lifetime) of public service. Native children were turned over to the Franciscan friars to be converted to Christianity. Acoma was not rebuilt until the late 1640s.[3]

In the earliest days of their conquest of the Americas, the Spaniards implemented a policy called *encomienda* which had built upon the *repartimiento* a labor system allowing settlers to use Indian labor. The encomienda imposed the obligation of giving religious education to the Indians in addition to the imposed slave labor. In 1512, the crown relented a bit and the Law of Burgos established the colonial principles that Indians were free individuals who would be converted to Christianity, work under the encomienda, and be supported and treated well. Yet the practical realities of imposing imperial rule over such distance and under such physical hardship as existed in the northern provinces of Mexico meant the law was not enforced. In fact, huge encomienda grants were given to the most elite conquistadors as reward for their service.

The Catholic Church developed theological justification for the mistreatment of Indians, believing it necessary to treat the natives in this manner for their own good to prepare them as civilized productive Christians. The treatment of the Pueblo Indians under this system and their punishment by the Franciscan friars for their belief in the old Kachina religion were probably the primary contributors to the unrest that led to the revolt of 1680.[4] Unlike the recently conquered provinces farther south, New Mexico did not provide the economic foundation based upon silver mining. Juan Onate's father Cristobal had grown wealthy mining silver in the Zacateca Province. The lack of resources in New Mexico brought conflict between the civil authorities and the church as both the friars and the settlors exploited the local Indian villages for labor and goods.

Several legends had developed about Mount Chalchihuitl. In an article written by Blake in 1858 he stated:

It is said that the Indians have a tradition that eight or nine of their tribe were once suddenly buried by a fall of rocks from the side of the great pit. Since that time they have been afraid to work in it.[5]

Legends concerning Spanish mining at the pit began in the early 1860s, and by the 1880s had grown to include the Aztecs as the original miners pursuing both turquoise and precious metals. The legend of "The Great Mine Collapse" leading to the Pueblo Revolt of 1680 was promoted to insinuate that Mount Chalchihuitl had been the site of significant Spanish mining operations in the past.[6] One version of the legend said a rockslide in 1680 buried 40 or so native Puebloans enslaved by the Spanish in their greedy quest for riches. When the oppressors attempted to draft replacements, the incident sparked the Pueblo Revolt that drove the Spanish south to El Paso, Texas. In her 1888 book, *The Land of the Pueblos,* Susan E. Wallace, wife of New Mexico Governor Lew Wallace, wrote that following the collapse of the wall resulting in the deaths of many Indian miners, the Spaniards attempted to requisition more miners from the nearby pueblo of San Marcos and this initiated the uprising, although she adds, "I give the tale for what it is worth," which indicates her skepticism of the oral tradition.[7]

In 1908, Fayette Jones stated, "Economic cruelty of the Spaniards inflicted on the Indian miners and the caving of the profound turquoise working at Mount Chalchihuitl, that killed a large number of slaves, caused a general uprising of the Pueblo Indians in 1680."[8]

The Spanish remained in El Paso until 1692 when Governor Don Diego de Vargas re-established their presence. During this 12-year absence, the Indians were said to have filled and hid all the mines and allowed the Spanish to return upon the promise of no more slavery in the mines.

Mining is and always has been a dangerous business, and it is quite probable a number of people were killed over the many years of activity on Mount Chalchihuitl. D.C. Hyde claimed to have uncovered skeletons in his mining operations in 1880. Although the Spanish worked the local silver mines, it is doubtful they worked the area for turquoise. They held turquoise in low esteem and considered the natives foolish to place such high value on it. The settlers were few in number and hard pressed to feed themselves, and they most certainly used forced labor from the Pueblos for personal service and to obtain food.

The natives resented the Franciscan friars, who had established a secular power and clerical presence in the colony, because they rejected the native Kachina religion. There is no indication they engaged in mining activities. The Pueblo Revolt of 1680 was planned over time, following the Acoma Revolt of 1599, the Jemez Revolt in 1614, and the 1639–1640 Revolt of the Taos, Picuris, and Jemez Pueblos. The Revolt of 1680 occurred for a number of reasons, including oppression, climate, disease, and religion, all of which contributed to economic hardship. A mine collapse and forced slavery at Mount Chalchihuitl was not likely the prime provocation.

Looking south toward Mount Chalchihuitl four miles north of Cerrillos. Cliffs are walls of main ancient working about 100 feet higher than the dump in the center and right of the picture. The pit is 105 feet deep on the upper side, 35 feet deep on the lower side; nearly 100 feet across in the bottom and over 200 feet across the rim. June, 1911. D.B. Sterrett, *U.S. Geological Survey*, 391.

Ancient turquoise works on Mount Chalchihuitl. Looking north across the ancient cut with old shaft in center behind the man in the pit.
June 1911. D.B. Sterrett, *U.S. Geological Survey*, 53.

Unlike the eastern United States, most of the land in the West was publicly owned. The Homestead Act provided a path to land ownership. Any citizen over the age of 21 could acquire property provided they lived on the land, built a home, and maintained a farm or ranch on the property for five years. The General Mining Act of 1872 allowed any citizen of the United States to acquire the right to mine for specified minerals on public lands. The steps were to locate a claim on the ground and post corner markers indicating the claim boundaries, and then filing, or locating, with the mining district or county recorder. A claim owner needed to prove economically viable minerals were on the claim, and file annual assessment paperwork showing a minimum investment of $100 in either time or expense to develop it. A claim could be sold or transferred through a recorded deed, providing all assessment work was up to date. An unpatented claim allowed the owner to extract the subterranean minerals, but ownership of the surface land remained public domain. Additional surveys and expense were involved to patent a claim, wherein the U.S. government deeded both the surface and mineral rights to the claimant as private property. The claimant then had full ownership of the land and it was placed on the county tax rolls. The claims discuss in our narrative were at first unpatented, but over time many of them were patented.

During the Spanish colonial period, sporadic mining was evident around Santa Fe, but never on a large-scale basis. Around 1821 a Mexican sheepherder discovered gold deposits in the Ortiz Mountains, and by 1830 a large mining camp had been established. Large quantities of coal were found in Madrid, New Mexico in 1835. The gold boom was short-lived, but Madrid continued to provide coal to the area well into the twentieth century. During the 1850s and 1860s, the Delgado family, as part of a Spanish Land Grant, claimed the Cerrillos Hills area. The claim was later rejected and the U.S. government opened the area to purchase in 1870. Some silver mining had been ongoing since 1861, but transportation of ore was a problem. Aware that the eventual arrival of the railroad could make even marginal mining profitable, Dr. Enos Andrews, a local dentist, and other Santa Fe entrepreneurs purchased 2,000 acres containing old Spanish silver mines and the ancient Mount Chalchihuitl turquoise mine.

In 1878, these businessmen hired Leadville, Colorado mining expert Robert Hart to open some of the silver workings in the Arroyo de las Minas area. Although in their employment, Hart did some personal prospecting on the adjacent public domain land opened by the new 1872 mining laws that expanded the ability to file claims on mining rights on public land. When he discovered promising silver ore, he resigned and returned to Leadville, possibly seeking support in case he encountered opposition from his former employers. Hart convinced friends and fellow miners such as Frank Demick to return to New Mexico—the cold weather and deep snowfall in the high Rocky Mountains made recruitment easy. By January of 1879, the Colorado miners had staked claims in the Cerrillos Hills.[9] In early 1880, the site of Demick and Hart's camp, three miles north of Cerrillos, had 40 or so structures and by February they named it Carbonateville.

To protect their interests, Dr. Andrews and his partners met on March 14, 1879 and established the Galisteo Mining District. Thirteen days later Hart and the Colorado miners met to form the Los Cerrillos Mining District. A meeting of miners was held at Carbonateville on July 5, 1880 to unite the Cerrillos, Galisteo, and Gonzales (Turquoise Hill) districts as the Cerrillos District. The southern boundary was established as the north boundary of the Ortiz Grant; the northern boundary as the Rio Chiquito; the eastern boundary as the county line; and the western boundary as the Rio Grande River.[10]

During this time, an unsuccessful attempt was made to change the name Carbonateville to Turquoise City (Turquesa) and to make it the center of the district, but the name did not stick. More importantly, the area was not as wealthy as first thought, which became evident by 1882, and by 1885 the rush was over. The lack of success in the mines and the shortage of water in the camps could not be overcome. By the mid-1880s, the town site was all but abandoned. Silver prices declined in the late 1880s and the economic crash of 1893 brought the closure of what few mines remained.[11]

D.C. Hyde and Mount Chalchihuitl

In 1872, Enos Andrews purchased, among other Spanish silver properties, the no. 99 Cash Entry Patent that included the ancient turquoise mine Mount Chalchihuitl. In late 1879, Major D.C. Hyde, in association with other New York investors, acquired three of Andrew's mining claims covering the ancient Chalchihuitl pits. Hyde began commercial development on January 1, 1880 under the name Grand Reserve Consolidated Gold and Silver Mining Company. As the name implies, the operation was undertaken to locate gold and silver deposits. As early as 1858, Blake had reported:

...there are no indications of [precious metals] ores at the locality. The sides of the pits were carefully examined whether it was possible that the excavation had been in part made for ores of the precious metals, but it was evident that the Chalchihuitl [turquoise] was the only mineral which had been sought for.[12]

At the time, American turquoise had no commercial value in non-native society. The Persian non-matrix, sky blue stone was considered the only turquoise of value, and no sensible businessperson would have considered investing in its poor American cousin. George Kunz, in his capacity as chief gemologist for Tiffany and Co., opined that American turquoise was not suitable as a gemstone because it had a tendency to change color from blue to green, an opinion he soon altered.

Hyde opened vertical shafts on the east and west sides of Mount Chalchihuitl intending to connect them via subterranean tunnels. The eastern shaft, no. 1, was 72 feet deep with a drift known as the Turquoise Tunnel that extended 18 of the 304 feet needed to connect the two shafts.[13] The western shaft, no. 2, was sunk through 73 feet of prehistoric debris and 15 feet of bedrock, and a drift called the Ore Tunnel was then driven 110 feet toward the eastern shaft.[14]

Hyde's promises of rich mineral wealth from these operations were never realized. Drawing attention to the Native American excavations was probably his only true success. During his excavations ancient stopes were uncovered on the east and west sides of the mountain. He claimed the eastern location contained veins of turquoise up to two inches thick and gold-bearing quartz.[15] Dubbed the "Wonder Caves," this is probably the only true prehistoric adit on Mount Chalchihuitl. A portion of this area may have been expanded to accommodate a museum set up to impress potential investors and tourists with the quantity of tools and artifacts recovered at the site.[16]

Near the western shaft another sealed area was discovered and named the Mystery.[17] All the other adits on Mount Chalchihuitl appear to have been excavated during this time (1880–1881). Their rectangular shape and dimensions are typical of territorial mining techniques. It is obvious these miners were solely in pursuit of precious metals because when they encountered a turquoise seam 40 feet into a southern adit, they made no effort to follow it. All the drifts appear to be exploratory, and very little turquoise was actually mined. About the only possible exploration for turquoise was a 10-foot drift in the rear of the Wonder Caves.[18]

False precious metal assays were created to stimulate the sale of stock.

As this failed to produce viable results, Hyde increased promotion of the turquoise deposits. From the beginning turquoise was shipped to New York, but the quality was marginal at best and too thin to be of commercial value. In fact, some of this material may have come from other sources such as the Old Castilian that Hyde also operated at that time.[19]

In 1880, New York stock promoters hired a Yale University geology professor named Benjamin Silliman to prepare reports on Mount Chalchihuitl and other New Mexico mining properties. He was considered a mining authority and charged top dollar for his services. In exchange, he had a tendency to exaggerate the facts in the interest of his employers. Silliman's articles were used to advance the fame and stimulate stock sales in the East.[20]

Mount Chalchihuitl at the time of Hyde mining activity, 1880-1882. Photo Bennet and Brown. Courtesy of Palace of the Governors Photo Archives (NMHM/DCA), 014827.

During the 1880s, all mining activity in the Cerrillos District was directed toward finding deposits of gold and silver. If turquoise was found, it was ignored because the price for the mineral was so low it did not pay to bring it to market. During the 1880s, the price for turquoise was equal to that of anthracite coal. In 1882, Kunz stated in the United States Geological Survey (USGS) *MRUS* report: "All the American turquoise is sold to either tourists or collectors or to the jewelry trade only as oddities."[21]

Yet the market for turquoise changed. The following chart is from USGS data as reported in MRUS reports. These are estimates—actual production most certainly was different. This is especially true for the boom years of the 1890s because mines were taxed on production and it was in the interest of claim holders to understate output. What is most important is the relation of the production by year with an increase of almost 500 percent in 1891 from the previous year. The economic conditions for mining turquoise had changed dramatically.

Turquoise Production Chart

1883 – $2,000

1884 – $2,000

1885 – $3,000

1886 – $3,000

1887 – $2,500

1888 – $3,000

1889 – $23,675

1890 – $28,675

1891 – $150,000

1892 – $175,000

1893 – $143,136

1894 – $34,000

1895 – $50,000

1896 – $40,000

1897 – $55,000

1898 – $50,000

1899 – $72,000

1900 – $82,000

1901 – $118,000

1902 – $130,000

1903 – $110,000

1904 – $100,000

1905 – $65,000

1906 – $22,840

1907 – $23,840

1908 – $147,950

1909 – $179,273

1910 – $85,900

1911 – $44,751

1912 – $10,140

1913 – $8,075

1914 – $13,370

1915 – $11,691

1916 – $21,811

1917 – $14,171

1918 – $20,667

1919 – $17,700

1920 – $4,869

1921 – $1,450

Milford states that the MRUS numbers for production provided by Kunz differ from those Territorial Governor Otero gave to the Secretary of the Interior as New Mexico's official figures.[22] The USGS numbers are certainly understated, and the governor's production amounts are likely more in line with actual production. It should be noted that in today's dollars, $475,000 would be almost $16.5MM and this would be the wholesale cost. We may assume that the finished retail value would be perhaps as high as $30MM in current value.

Year	Total for all U.S. (USGS)	Total for New Mexico Only
1891	$150,000	$150,000
1892	$175,000	$175,000
1893	$143,000	$200,000
1894	$34,000	$250,000
1895	$50,000	$350,000
1896	$40,000	$475,000

We cannot be certain of the cause of this huge increase in the demand for turquoise. We know that in the 1893 MRUS report, which covered calendar year 1892, Kunz wrote:

During the past two years turquoise has been actively mined by two companies, the American Turquoise Company and the Azure Turquoise Company; a few minor attempts by others have been made. The first of the two above-named companies, engaged in mining 6 miles from Los Cerrillos, New Mexico, reopening some of the mines originally worked by the Indians, and have found turquoise equal in color to the finest Persian material. Its stability in retaining color is equally great, not changing within a short time, as does the Egyptian turquoise, which was so extensively placed on the market about the time when the Persian mines were ceasing to yield.[23]

In this MRUS report, Kunz goes on to relate his findings on a trip to Persian, searching unsuccessfully for turquoise. Speaking in the third person, Kunz made these comments:

He returned to the United States, giving up the projected trip, and purchasing only the finest gems, as nearly all the material shown, although held at high prices, was not up to the standard of the American turquoise. Stones have been found at these new localities weighing up to 60 carats each, one of which was sold for about $4,000; and it is now possible for the first time in the past half century to match a perfect turquoise necklace.

Kunz is less enthusiastic about the turquoise of the Azure mines in Grant County, saying that although it is a robin's egg blue it has a "faint greenish tinge" and is not of the same sky blue as that of Cerrillos. We may gather from this comment that, in this case, Kunz was speaking more as chief gemologist of Tiffany and Co., the president of which, Charles Lewis Tiffany, was also a bondholder and stockholder in the ATC, than in his role with the USGS and this was a none-too-gentle jibe at a competing turquoise company.

Turquoise production in Persia was decreasing and the preferred non-matrix, sky blue grade was becoming more and more difficult to obtain. Tiffany had established Tiffany Blue° as his principal marketing brand, displayed through his signature Blue Box and the firm's mail order *Blue Book.* Kunz had accumulated for Tiffany and Co. a collection of gems that included many examples from the United States, with at least three turquoise specimens from Cerrillos. The Tiffany collection of precious gems was shown at the Paris expositions of 1889 and 1900. J. Pierpont Morgan purchased the collection and gave it to the American Museum of Natural History. In addition, a July 31, 1890 article from the *Santa Fe Daily New Mexican* stated Kunz was in Santa Fe with Adolph F. Bandelier to visit the turquoise mines and promote his book, *Gems and Precious Stones of North America,* in which Cerrillos turquoise was mentioned. This was an important visit and may be regarded as perhaps the beginning of The Great American Turquoise Rush. We must speculate as to Kunz's motives for his visit, whether it was purely scientific or as an agent for Tiffany and Co. to determine if the Cerrillos turquoise could be a replacement for increasingly expensive turquoise sourced from Persia. In any case, soon after his visit interest in turquoise mining increased in the area, perhaps driven by the desire to prove its availability and quality to east coast investors.

During periods of low demand, producers had little incentive to mine turquoise because prices did not provide sufficient profit to justify the expense of mining something that formed randomly in veins that could disappear with no indication of where additional formations might be located. Also, unlike precious metals such as gold, silver, and copper that typically existed in measurable quantities and had industrial as well as esthetic uses, turquoise was valued solely as a collectible and an adornment.

The resurgence of interest in turquoise from the United States was initiated by events occurring across the globe in Persia. According to Khazeni, during the 1880s attempts were made to reclaim the old turquoise mines of Khurasan Province, including the famed mines of Nishapur, through a state run monopoly.[24] Local miners and traders had operated the mines for centuries, and they resented state control that rendered them government employees. This, coupled with high taxes imposed by the Shah, reduced economic incentive and productivity dropped. Many mines were abandoned and deteriorated but demand for Persian turquoise remained high in Europe and other markets. The reduced output caused a dramatic rise in prices that influenced Kunz's 180-degree change in his assessment of New Mexico turquoise as a true gemstone in the 1893 MRUS report, and The Great American Turquoise Rush began.

During the 1880s, Hyde was attempting to develop a market for turquoise in New York, presumably through his east coast investors. These investors, of whom Tiffany and Co. was perhaps the largest, most likely were unable to meet demand for turquoise jewelry and were looking for a new source. The example of Victorian jewelry in the Introduction showed turquoise was popular, especially when combined in settings with diamonds and other gems.

We can also assume that those in the jewelry trade understood the best way to maximize profit in a retail consumer market was to vertically integrate the different phases of extraction, processing, wholesale distribution, fabrication, and retail distribution. By controlling each phase of the process, from locating and mining the turquoise to selling jewelry through their worldwide distribution of retail stores and growing mail order business, they could profit from each step. As investors from the major capital markets of New York and Chicago competed with each other to establish a controlling presence in a market with limited supply, they created the stimulus that started The Great American Turquoise Rush. Investors that controlled the source of production would enjoy a significant advantage in the marketplace.

George F. Kunz. Public domain

Charles Lewis Tiffany was an iconic figure during his time, and the Tiffany brand continues to demand a premium presence and price in the marketplace. Tiffany extended his market beyond New York City in 1845 with the publication of the first Tiffany *Blue Book,* so named for the book's distinctive robin's egg blue cover, chosen in response to the traditional color for brides or possibly because of the popularity of turquoise in nineteenth-century jewelry. Sometime after this, the famous Tiffany Blue Box was introduced. As reported by the *New York Sun* in 1906:

> Tiffany has one thing in stock that you cannot buy of him for as much money as you may offer, he will only give it to you. And that is one of his boxes. The rule of the establishment is ironclad, never to allow a box bearing the name of the firm to be taken out of the building except with an article which has been sold by them and for which they are responsible.

Tiffany and Co., Tiffany, the color Tiffany Blue, and the Tiffany Blue Box are trademarks of Tiffany and Co.

Although Tiffany and Young started out offering stationary and dry goods, they soon switched to jewelry and silverware, but the *Blue Book* continued to offer many household items.

Prices ranged from a low of $2.50 ($65 in current dollars) for a small child's turquoise ring to $100 ($2,600 in current dollars) for a larger turquoise and diamond setting. Considering that the per carat prices for non-matrix, sky blue—high-grade—turquoise would have exceeded $10 per carat (approximately $260 in current dollars), we can surmise the total carat weight of these settings was small. In his book, *The Turquois,* Joseph E. Pogue makes the following observations about turquoise prices:

> At the present time (1914) the turquois is out of fashion and not very popular in the United States. Consequently its value is down and $10 a carat for good quality is an average price. This applies only to stones of a few carats weight; larger ones of the finest grade are worth more per carat. Turquois matrix, according to quality, brings up to about $1 per carat.[25]

Pogue goes on to reference sources during the time of The Great American Turquoise Rush that attributed prices for high-grade from the Azure Company of $5–10 per carat, which had risen by 1907 to between $6 and $25, with an average price of $15. When calculated in today's dollars, the current highest-grade turquoise is not significantly overpriced.

Although the ATC was important because it was responsible for the mining and sale of a large amount of turquoise during the 1890s, another contribution to the story of turquoise was the imprint Tiffany left on the company and a score of other turquoise mines in the Southwest. Although he was invested in the initial company as a creditor and probably as a stockholder after December 1892, his name continues in the presence of innumerable turquoise mines throughout the Southwest. In fact, Tiffany never made a claim in his own name and while it is certainly true that much of the production from these "Tiffany" mines found their way to the retail market through Tiffany and Co., the actual claims were made by others who found it in their economic interest to associate their turquoise mine with a successful brand like Tiffany. Tiffany and Co. bought a lot of turquoise during The Great American Turquoise Rush,

but neither he nor his company ever owned a claim or operated a
indirectly involved as a bondholder and stockholder in the ATC,
the Tiffany—Muñiz—claim in Cerrillos and a Tiffany claim in
the ATC did not develop. This is a recurring theme in the mark
products in the United States, as evidenced by our use of Kleene
to name two. Tiffany Blue® is a potent marketing tool and many have sought to
attach their turquoise efforts to the brand.

A little north of the main body of the Cerrillos Hills lays a small, low
group of hills commonly referred to as Turquoise Hill. This area has been the
scene of turquoise mining for hundreds of years. The hills lie on the southern
edge of a prairie that extends to the city of Santa Fe and the base of the Sangre
de Christo Mountains. Rumors of an ancient turquoise mine in these hills
encouraged veteran miner Michael O'Neil to travel to New Mexico from Leadville, Colorado in 1878, only to find this claim, the Old Castilian, had already
been located by the time he arrived.[26] It is unknown whether his interest was
inspired by Robert Hart or if it came from other sources. We are also unsure
when or for what minerals the Old Castilian had been located previously, but
on December 5, 1879 Hugh Marshall and James Franklin Callender located
the Old Castilian as part of a group of claims staked on what became known
as the Marshall Hills. This was perhaps the first staked turquoise mining claim
in the United States. Although O'Neil was not part of this claim, he played an
important role in the ongoing effort to mine turquoise in Cerrillos over the
next 20 years.

Marshall and Callender are important for their early contribution to the
development of turquoise mining, although others built upon these efforts.
Callender moved in 1879 from Missouri to Cerrillos and was active during the
mining boom years there. He became the second and last U.S. Postmaster of
the nearby mining community of Bonanza, the state's 13th oldest post office.
Today a large ranch and movie set exist on what was the site of Bonanza.

Hugh Marshall had a more checkered background. Soon after his collaboration with Callender it was discovered his real name was Edward Eggleston,
an alleged murderer who jumped bail in Colorado and was hiding in Cerrillos.
He was arrested in Albuquerque but escaped to parts unknown.

Northwest towards Old Castilian turquoise mine, June 1911.
D.B. Sterrett, *U.S. Geological Survey*, 401.

As we have noted, no turquoise was actively mined in the Cerrillos area during the 1880s because of lack of demand and low prices. This began to change with the interest of speculators in the area at the end of the decade.

The variety and availability for investment we enjoy today did not exist in the United States during the Victorian era. Most equity investments were held by a few financiers who had near, if not outright monopoly, control over their respective market. Examples of this are Andrew Carnegie in steel, John D. Rockefeller in oil, and Cornelius Vanderbilt in railroads. Most investments were debt securities issued by lenders as bonds with the financed corporate assets held as collateral.

In this environment, the opportunity for wealth focused upon the rapidly expanding western United States, with huge amounts of capital going into the creation of infrastructure, primarily railroads, and mineral exploration needed to fuel the nation's rapidly growing industrial output. Young entrepreneurs were encouraged to "Go West, young man," first stated by John Babsone Lane Soule in an 1851 editorial in the *Terre Haute Express,* "and grow up with the country." Horace Greeley later used the quote in his own editorial in 1865.[27]

Two such investors were Chauncey G. Story and James M. Allan , who was married to Story's sister, Eleanor. They were both from Illinois and were known to have connections with New York jewelers. Story and Allan began to acquire claims specifically for mining turquoise. James M. Allen moved to Santa Fe with his brothers John and Alex in about 1883. John was involved in developing a local ore smelter. The deeds of the Muñiz and Castilian that transferred from the Muñiz brothers to Eleanor Story Allan, and then back to Chauncey Story, and finally the ATC, witnessed by both John and Alex Allan, show the brothers were working together on various mining prospects. The family relationship was further complicated by the fact that Eleanor was also the name of John Allan's wife. Both Eleanor Story Allan 'and Eleanor H. Allan are named in the transfer of the Muñiz claim to Chauncey Story on January 27, 1892. The deed was witnessed by James M. Allan and Alex H. Allan and notarized by John D. Allan. Alex Allan became a Santa Fe County deputy sheriff and was murdered in 1897 during a dispute at the Bottom Dollar Mine, a claim he was working in the Cerrillos Hills south of Turquoise Hill.

One of the early mining ventures of John D. Allan was the Santa Fe Gem Company. The articles of incorporation were filed on April 15, 1885, and the members of the board of directors were John Grey, Thomas Moore, Sr., John D. Allan, Milton K. Parmaly, and David L. Miller, all well known in the local mining area. Moore was an associate of M.W. Porterfield of Silver City. The articles of incorporation state the objective of the location, purchase, development, and sale of precious gems and stones of every description, with specific mention of turquoise. Although the articles noted erecting a smelter for processing metal ores, turquoise was mentioned no less than three times, giving a good indication that the boom in metal mining was waning while prospects for turquoise were on the rise. At the time, 1885, there was little market for turquoise, thus it is not surprising the company did not proceed with any notable mining activity, although the Shah claim in the Cerrillos Hills was located in June 1885 by Thomas Moore, Sr., John Gray, and John D. Allen.

It is interesting to note that in an age where corporate interests, many financed by east coast investors, were the central means for turquoise mining during The Great American Turquoise Rush, the first company formed was by local miners in the Santa Fe area. Perhaps the interest of the Santa Fe Gem Company came from the influence of Milton Parmaly, who was very involved with the Old Castilian claim.

According to Milford,[28] Parmaly sold the Old Castilian to Hiram B. Cartwright for $1,000 on February 20, 1889. Cartwright in turn sold the claim to Story and Allan for an undocumented amount, and they recorded title in the name of Eleanor A. Allan on April 23, 1890 in Book I, page 18 of the Santa Fe County Records of Mining Deeds. A deed from her to her brother was not located, but Chauncey G. Story conveyed the Old Castilian to the ATC (Illinois Corp.) by mining deed dated March 5, 1892, and filed March 19, 1892. This deed covered the Old Castilian and Muñiz along with the other three claims Story and Allan had made. Those three were the Morningstar, located June 2, 1891 by James M. Allan, and the two located by Story, the Sky Blue located on November 2, 1891, and the Gem located June 2, 1891. Title to all five claims as of March 1892 was in the name of the ATC.

Only the Castilian and Muñiz were mined for turquoise, and the Muñiz became known as the Tiffany. The other claims served as a buffer and were not worked other than to meet the annual maintenance requirements to retain the claims. Hugh Marshall leased the Old Castilian to O'Neil in 1880. Whatever mining done on the property prior to 1889 was in search of materials other than turquoise because its low price provided little economic incentive. After leasing the property to O'Neil, Marshall sold the claim to M.K. Parmaly who, after about 18 months in 1881, did not renew O'Neil's lease and held the claim throughout the 1880s—although he may have leased the property to others during that time. The area containing the Muñiz claim was worked intermittently during the 1880s, including by James F. Callender, but all of these claims were abandoned until January 31, 1890 when the Muñiz brothers worked the mine, and then sold the part of the claim containing the mineshaft to the Storys in 1891. For a short while, Faustin lived in the small cabin he and his brother Pedro had built, grazing goats until the brothers sold the remainder of the claim to the Storys.[29] Perhaps Pedro used the proceeds from the sale of the mine to enter the growing curio trade in Santa Fe that had been developing since the railroad's arrival opened the sleepy town to increased tourism. He was known to have been a curio dealer in the 1890s and briefly entered into a business relationship with one of the original Santa Fe curio dealers, Jake Gold, in 1904 shortly before Gold's death.[30] The Muñiz claim was patented by the ATC in 1915 and is currently owned by Douglas Magnus, a Santa Fe artist and jewelry designer.

Before their transfer of the Muñiz to the ATC, it seemed Story and Allan had every intention of working the claims, perhaps if only to demonstrate their value to potential buyers. A report from the *Cerrillos Rustler* from May 29, 1891 mentioned that James Allan of Chicago came in from his turquoise camp at Bonanza with C.G. Story, who had been in charge of the camp for the previous year, and that regular shipments of turquoise were made monthly to Chicago and New York because the popularity of their stone "makes it easy to dispose of their product at good prices."[31] Bonanza was a small city located six miles north of Cerrillos near Turquoise Hill where Story and Allan had their claims. The city had a mill which was used to crush the metal ore before processing at a smelter where it was heated and made into a finished product. More importantly, it was the nearest source for water. They hired John Maddox of nearby Carbonateville to manage the operation, until tragedy struck. Around 6 p.m. on August 24, 1891, Maddox was being lifted from the Muñiz shaft and lighting black powder fuses as he ascended. Near the top of the shaft the rope broke, and Maddox dropped about 60 feet and the charges detonated above him. When his fellow workers reached him he could barely say, "This is the end of me." Maddox died just after midnight with his last words being that no one was to blame.[32] Work was suspended and just over four months later, Story sold the claims to the ATC. Although it might seem this tragedy motivated Story and Allan to sell the claim, closer examination reveals this as mainly a business decision. It's feasible they recognized that the operation required more investment and management than they were willing or able to make.

The ATC was incorporated in the State of Illinois on February 27, 1892 following initial filing on January 29. The charter reveals corporate stock was capitalized initially at a value of $1.6MM, with Chauncey Story the principal owner with 15,990 shares and James and Eleanor Allan each owning five shares. A subsequent filing lists the initial board of directors as John R. Andrews, Joseph G. Doty, Chauncey G. Story, and J. Edwards Fay.

Doty and Andrews

John Rutt Andrews' father George and his uncle John were jewelers in New York. In 1854, they were making jewelry exclusively for Tiffany and Co. By 1862, John R. Andrews was in charge of the firm when his father retired. In 1870, Tiffany and Co. purchased Andrews' entire operation and Andrews became a stockholder in the company, managing the jewelry manufacturing department. In 1882, he left the firm and became a stockbroker in partnership with A. De Cordova. Five years later, in 1887, he sold all of his Tiffany stock for a sum reported to be $400,000[33] (over $18 million in 2016 value) and formed a partnership with Joseph G. Doty as wholesale dealers in diamonds and precious stones.[34] In a November 25, 1888 *New York Times* article titled, "Accused by His Father, A Well Known Stock Broker's Disappearance" it is reported that Andrews owed his father $50,000 and was reportedly hiding in Paris:

Mr. Andrews, who is 45, was known among Wall Street brokers as quite a "sport." He was supposedly very wealthy, lived in luxurious style, and kept a yacht and fast horses. Andrews' father accuses him of fraud and failure to pay a loan.

Less is known about the background of Doty. He was born in New Jersey in 1844 and ran away from home at the age of 16, reportedly traveling extensively. Doty's daughter Hazel stated he sat for entrance exams to West Point when he was 16 and, although accepted, ran away while traveling to the academy. Evidently Doty had no interest in being a soldier.[35] He was a jeweler and appraiser working in New York and presumably was well known to John Andrews and the Tiffany organization. The firm of Andrews and Doty was appointed sole agent for the ATC, responsible for the sale and distribution of all the turquoise mined, although it is likely that Doty did most of the work.

Andrews was the first president of the ATC, with Doty serving on the board of directors. According to the *New York Times,* the company was expected to have a monopoly of the turquoise business and would handle the entire output of the company's mines.[36] Although the output of turquoise was increasing, the company encountered financial difficulties from the very beginning of its operation.

A New Superintendent at Turquoise Hill

Work had been suspended at the Muñiz claim since the John Maddux's death in August 1891. When the claims were transferred to the newly incorporated ATC in early 1892, the operation needed a new mining superintendent and Chauncey Story had just the man for the job, miner James Patrick McNulty. He arrived in Cerrillos in early 1892 and began work by mid-year, overseeing a crew of three to five miners. McNulty was a hands-on manager who set the explosive charges himself, participated in the backbreaking work of removing material from the shaft and helped with the time-consuming task of sorting and picking out suitable turquoise. He was meticulous in his recordkeeping.[37] His correspondence with the managers of the ATC shows the pressure McNulty was under from the very beginning to provide the quality turquoise the market demanded.

The ATC was financed by bonds issued by Farmers' Loan and Trust Company of New York in the amount of $250,000 and secured by the deeds to the turquoise mines the company owned. Several wealthy New Yorkers invested in the company through the purchase of these bonds, including the sons of Allen Pinkerton of the Pinkerton Detective Agency, James Stillman, president of the New York City Bank, and Charles Lewis Tiffany.[38]

Unfortunately for the company, while turquoise prices had risen dramatically, the Panic of 1893 and the resulting economic recession kindled unemployment, a stock market decline, bank failures, and a weakened desire for capital investment. John Andrews, whose lavish lifestyle included a private yacht, was financially affected by a series of poor investments and dubious stock deals, and the pressure may have been the contributing factor in his death in March 1894.

Financial pressure continued for the company. Although output was high, with sales well in excess of $60,000 per year, demands for cash were high. The mine's operating expenses were about $500 per month. The loan needed to be repaid, and the shareholders demanded dividends for their investment. In December 1892, the ATC declared a dividend of six cents a share on $1MM of capital stock for the preceding six months. The original capitalization of 16,000 shares had been reduced to 10,000 on July 8, 1892, which meant that shareholders received a payment of $600. At the date of the original incorporation, Story owned the vast majority of shares with James A. Allan and his wife holding a token amount. When the number of shares was reduced, that proportionately reduced the number of shareholder shares.

A December 24, 1892 report in the *New York Times* declared the six-cent per share dividend of the ATC, listing a capitalization of $1MM with the shareholders consisting of Charles L. Tiffany; M. Billings of Randall, Baremore and Billings; W.M. Alling; John R. Andrews, president of Andrews and Doty; and James A. Allan of Chicago." We must speculate as to the possible meaning of this report. First of all, newspaper reports are often incorrect and the reporter may have confused bond owners of the company with stockholders. Yet the parties named indicate another possibility. Perhaps following the reduction in the number of shares, Story sold his shares to Tiffany, Billings, Alling, Andrews, and Allan. In the book, *Tiffany Blue,* Story's involvement with the company following the appointment of McNulty as the superintendent is mentioned rarely and, after 1892, he is not mentioned at all. If this scenario were true, then Charles L. Tiffany was not only a bondholder of the original ATC, but also a stockholder. Randall, Baremore and Billings was the largest importer of diamonds in America, with offices on the corner of Maiden Lane and Nassau in the heart of the jewelry district. William Alling, a prominent east coast jeweler who had presumably purchased turquoise from the ATC, would have reason to invest in the operation. The involvement of Tiffany made sense as a means to leverage his bond investment in the firm and as part of a plan to dominate the turquoise market. Since James Allan originally held no stock of any consequence, he may have increased his small number of shares following the possible purchase from Story by the new shareholders. The newspaper account lists James Allan from Chicago, which indicates he may have relocated to his hometown as of that date or was identified with that city.

The ownership of both the bonds and stock would have been in the name of Charles L. Tiffany and not in the name of the corporation, Tiffany and Co., where he was certainly the principal shareholder as well as an officer and director. Ownership by an individual is distinct and separate from corporate ownership. We may assume that Charles L. Tiffany, a very wealthy man, would have, in addition to his ownership of shares in Tiffany and Co., many other investments of stocks and bonds including those of the ATC. In a letter dated June 7, 1962, William Fielding, a Tiffany and Co. spokesperson, wrote to Merrill Murphy:

> In reply to your letter of June 1, Tiffany and Co. has never owned or operated a turquoise mine in New Mexico or elsewhere. Any use of our name in connection with such ownership or operation is erroneous. From time to time during the past 40 years or so, inquiries have come to us from persons seeking information about a so-called "Tiffany Mine," variously located in the Santa Fe area, in Cerrillos, New Mexico, and in Villa Grove, Colorado. We have always informed the writers of these communications that Tiffany and Co. never had any connection with such a mine. What may have led to some confusion is that about sixty years ago we took over a few shares of stock in the "American Turquoise Company" in partial payment of a debt which was owing to us. At various times after that we sold a few turquoise (the product of this mine) cut for setting in jewelry, but know nothing further about it and believe it went out of business many years ago. The securities which we held in this connection were marked off years ago as worthless.[39]

Charles Lewis Tiffany died February 18, 1902, and his son and successor, artist and designer Louis Comfort Tiffany, had ideas that differed from those of his father. His interest in glass and modern jewelry design moved the company in the direction for which it has come to be recognized. We may speculate that following his death and the disposition of his estate there may have been some transfer of either the bonds or stock he held in the ATC to Tiffany and Co. It is clear that the ongoing use of the Tiffany name throughout the Southwest had no connection to either the individual or the company.

Stable cash flow is seldom associated with turquoise mining, where veins and pockets appear only to vanish with no indication as to where the next might be discovered. Eventually the financial pressures became too great, and early in 1897 the trust company foreclosed for the amount of $85,481.52. It is interesting to note that the ATC had paid down the original outstanding debt of $250,000 by $164,518.48 during the term of the debt from June of 1892 over the five-year period. We may speculate on how the ATC's financial affairs might have improved had the cash from operations been reinvested into the company. There were also contractual liabilities for gross commissions paid as part of a purchase arrangement for mines in Grant County, New Mexico that never proved profitable. In addition to the dividend paid in 1892 and the interest and principal payments on the note, McNulty had been paid operating expenses of about $500 a month. Assuming an interest rate of 3 percent on the bonds, an annual interest payment of about $7,000 would have been paid in addition to reduction of principal. From these numbers alone we may conclude that the Tiffany mine, over the five-year period before foreclosure, had generated cash flow of minimum between $250,000 and $300,000, all of which was absorbed by the liabilities of the company and was not available for reinvestment.

Howard Carter and William Alling were given control of the company as trustees for the bondholders. An associate of Stillman, Robert Parker, a major creditor that headed the credit department of Farmers' Loan and Trust Company, was put in charge of the mine operation. During a bankruptcy, the order of claims on the assets are general creditors followed by bondholders and, finally, stockholders. Although Doty remained involved with the newly organized company, he gradually faded from any involvement. The mine deeds were placed in trust for the bondholders—Stillman, the Pinkertons, and Tiffany.[40] This effectively ended the goal of the ATC to establish a turquoise monopoly in the Southwest. The following years brought several company reorganizations until the final descent into receivership and dissolution that began in 1915 shortly following the patent of the claims.

Throughout the difficulties, James Patrick McNulty remained as superintendent of the mines. His allegiance was rewarded in 1922. Through the long ordeal of receivership, McNulty had provided for the retention of the claims by paying the taxes on the property—which had been put on the tax rolls following the patent. In January he received communication from the bankruptcy trustees representing the sole remaining bondholders of the original company, the Pinkerton brothers, to sell the claims and retain one third of the net sales price. He continued to pay the property tax from 1922 to 1925. Finally, in March 1925, just past his 79th birthday, he received a telegram from his mining friend in Silver City, W.C. Porterfield, that he had found a buyer, Chester H. Smith of Boston. The price was $18,000, to be paid in $2000 installments, with Porterfield receiving a $100 commission from each payment.[41] McNulty's share was increased to one half, with the other presumably going to the trustees. McNulty died in 1933 at the age of 87. For an excellent account of the history of the ATC as detailed in the correspondence of James Patrick McNulty, read *Tiffany Blue* by Patricia McCraw.

View of Tiffany claim from the west with McNulty home, June 1911. D.B. Sterrett, ***U.S. Geological Survey,*** **404.**

James P. McNulty with his wife, daughter, and dogs in front of their home, June 1911.
D.B. Sterrett, *U.S. Geological Survey*, 408.

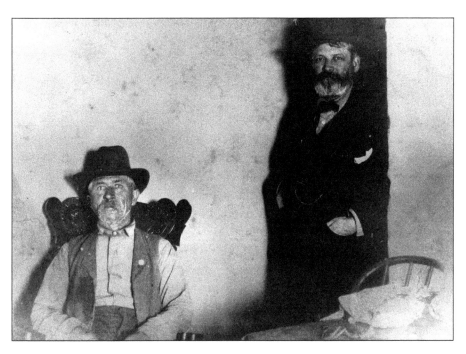

James Patrick McNulty and Joseph G. Doty, 1890s.
Courtesy of Arizona Historical Society, Tucson, 24322.

McNulty and Doty at Muñiz-Tiffany cabin, 1890s. This was the cabin the Muñiz brothers built. It is called a Jacal, where the logs are placed vertically, and then plastered with mud like an adobe.
Courtesy of Arizona Historical Society, Tucson, 24324.

The Land Grant Lawsuit

One of the ATC's problems that increased their financial troubles was the ongoing land grant trial, which took up much of the company's resources. Two Spanish land grant conflicts in the area of Turquoise Hill in the late 1890s and early 1900s concerned the Los Cerrillos Grant and the Jose de Leyba Grant.

The Los Cerrillos Grant was originally conveyed to Ensign Alonzo Rael de Agular in 1692 for "faithful military service" during the Spanish re-entry into New Mexico following the Great Pueblo Revolt of 1680. Land grants were a useful incentive to encourage Spanish settlers in Mexico to settle Nuevo Mexico, a difficult area in which to sustain a living. The memory of the 1680 Pueblo Revolt and the 1696 revolt following the return of de Vargas in 1692 also remained. Ongoing raids from not only Pueblo rebels, but also Navajo and Apache raiders, were an additional disincentive to settle in the area.

By 1804, the land had been acquired by Manuel Delgado and it was his heirs who in 1871 petitioned the U.S. Surveyor General for confirmation of the grant. It was recommended to Congress in 1872 for confirmation and initially surveyed in 1877. The original southern boundary was designated the Cerro Altos, or "high hills." It was in these hills that mining claims of the ATC and others were located in the 1880s and 1890s.

The original Los Cerrillos Grant survey of 1877 included parts of the Muñiz, Morning Star, and Castilian claims, but a new survey in 1896 moved the southern boundary a half mile to the north and the mines no longer conflicted with the grant. Although there had been controversy concerning the surface ownership of the Los Cerrillos Grant when the tract was confirmed and the patent issued on December 17, 1897, the mineral estate was retained by the U.S. government and remained open to the location of mining claims. It was the Jose de Leyba Grant that proved the more serious threat to the Turquoise Hills claims.

On May 24, 1728, Jose de Leyba of Santa Fe appeared before the Spanish governor of New Mexico to register a tract of land. This land was bounded on the north by property of Captain Sebastian de Vargas, on the east by the San Marcos Road, on the south by the arroyo called Cuesta del Oregano, and on the west by property of Juan Garcia de las Rivas. Registration of the land was granted under the condition that it be settled within the time frame prescribed by royal ordinance. The Leyba family was in active possession of the land until 1839, when Indians killed Jose de Leyba's great grandson Juan Angel de Leyba as he traveled to the gold fields south of the land grant, and it was then abandoned and mostly forgotten. Spanish land grants required the grant holder to live on the grant and continually work it, unlike mining claims.

Mariano F. Sena grew up in the house his father Jose built for his wife, Isabel Cabeza de Baca, in what is now known as Sena Plaza in downtown Santa Fe. Both Jose and Isabel came from prominent Castilian families. Jose was well-educated, fluent in English and Spanish, an attorney-at-law, and, in 1853, private secretary and interpreter for the territorial delegate to Washington from New Mexico. When the Civil War broke out, he raised a company, was mustered in as a captain, and participated in the battles of Glorietta, Peralta, Valverde, and the Indian campaigns of Kit Carson. In 1864, he was promoted to the rank of major. After the war, he was sheriff of Santa Fe County for twelve years and was registrar for the land office. Throughout his long career he was always a strong Republican.

Jose's son Mariano was born in Santa Fe in 1861. He was educated at St. Michael's College and graduated at the head of his class from the Jesuit Father's School in Las Vegas in 1882. He served as district court clerk and was the interpreter for Judge/Governor Axtell and the U.S. Indian Agency. In 1895, he became chief clerk for the House of Representatives of New Mexico Territory. Jose D. Sena II, Mariano's younger brother, also served in many political positions. He was a deputy U.S. Marshall, private secretary to Governor LeBaron Bradford Prince, a representative to the state legislature, and mayor of Santa Fe from 1908–1910. As clerk of the New Mexico Supreme Court for 33 years, he received many documents concerning the trials involving his brother.

Around 1894, an attorney friend of Mariano's named Purdy informed him of the existence of the Jose de Leyba Grant just south of Santa Fe. It had been uncovered by a search of the Spanish Archives of New Mexico for substantiating documentary evidence of the southern boundaries of the Sebastian de Vargas Land Grant.

At this time, the mines on Turquoise Hill were taking out a considerable amount of turquoise and Sena thought they might be within the boundaries of the Leyba grant. He began a search for the grant heirs and soon found two great-great grandchildren of the original grantee. He bought out their interest in the grant for an undisclosed amount. Sena and his attorneys then went on a "picnic" at the newly acquired grant.

While they were on the dumps of the turquoise mines, they were spotted and ordered off by J.P. McNulty, superintendent for the ATC. McNulty knew the men, shook hands all around, and offered to show them the mines. Asked the value of the turquoise being mined, McNulty answered, "Not less than $200,000." It was an impressive amount. Soon thereafter he learned of the existence of the land grant when he was served a court summons to a hearing regarding the validity of the grant. This was the beginning of 16 years of court trials.

Sena first filed suit in the Court of Private Land Claims on September 29, 1899 for confirmation of the Leyba grant he estimated contained 16,000 acres. The grant claim conflicted with the Los Cerrillos grant and the mining claims of the ATC and others, all of whom were made defendants in the suit. When the case went to trial on April 30 1900, Sena introduced documents from the Spanish Archives of New Mexico and the oral testimony of old-timers as proof that his purchase of the grant had been from the legitimate heirs.

The court cited a Spanish royal ordinance enacted in October of 1754 that required all land grants made after 1700 to apply for confirmation as a prerequisite of determining validity. No evidence was presented that this had been complied with; the grant was determined to be imperfect and, therefore, subject to U.S. requirements that a petition for confirmation be filed within two years of establishment, in 1891, with the Court of Private Land Claims. Neither action came to pass and the statute of limitations expired, which led the court to dismiss the case in favor of the defendants.

Sena appealed to the U.S. Supreme Court, intent on submitting new evidence he felt sufficient to form a conclusive presumption of compliance with the Royal Ordinance of 1754. His search of the Spanish Archives turned up the 1783 will of Simon de Leyba, son of Jose de Leyba, the original grantee. The will showed the family's active possession of the land 55 years after the grant and 29 years after the 1754 ordinance. The original papers had since been lost in the jumble of the archives, but Sena hoped the will proved compliance.

When the case was argued before the Supreme Court in 1903, the description of the grant boundaries was one of several stumbling blocks. The northern and eastern boundaries were definable, but the western and southern boundaries were vague. Any evidence of occupancy at the time of Juan Angel de Leyba's death in 1839 had totally eroded away. In the Anglo-Saxon legal system, abandonment questions are rare because abandoned land is usually sold on the open market or seized for taxes. Spanish colonial law recognized that landowners dissatisfied with their estates could abandon them and they became open to the next claimant. There had been no assertion of title for the grant in many years. Sena secured deed to the grant in 1895, two years past the Court of Private Lands deadline, and filed his case with the courts in 1899, six years after the deadline.

On April 6, 1903, the U.S. Supreme Court dismissed Sena's petition for failure to assert legal rights within a reasonable time. Sena motioned for a re-hearing and the decree was amended several months to allow further appeals. Sena brought an Action of Ejectment in New Mexico District Court against the ATC concerning its 50 acres of mining claims. The court found Sena had not proven his grant covered the disputed area, and found in favor of the defendant. He appealed the ruling to the Supreme Court of New Mexico Territory in 1907. The court found no proof of confirmation as required by the Royal Ordinance of 1754, that the western and southern boundaries of the grant had not been firmly established, and evidence of possession was too vague to raise a presumption in place of proof. The grant was ruled imperfect and time had expired to have it confirmed.

In Sena's 1911 U.S. Supreme Court appeal, the grant's boundaries again were a problem. Sena's case was built upon the theory that the western boundary of the Leyba Grant was a north-south line passing through a hill known as Penasco Blanco, but the Los Cerrillos Grant, which had already been confirmed, extended east of this line. Sena had not presented adequate evidence to firmly establish the grant's western and southern boundaries or to dispute the Los Cerrillos boundaries. The court ruled insufficient evidence existed to disturb the ATC's claims.

With this decision, the Jose de Leyba Land Grant controversy was finally laid to rest, but not the troubles of Mariano Sena. In 1900 he was appointed clerk for the U.S. Census Bureau where he was in charge of expense accounts to be sent to Washington, DC. Sena was accused of using a facsimile rubber stamp of his supervisor's signature to forge pay vouchers of real and fictitious census employees and cashing the bogus checks.

On September 16, 1902, Sena was convicted on four counts of forgery in District Court and sentenced to imprisonment for one year and one day for each count, to be served cumulatively, a total of four years four days. The case was twice taken to the Supreme Court of the Territory on appeal and from that court to the Circuit Court of Appeals, where the judgment was affirmed on February 26, 1912. Sena was re-sentenced on May 5, 1912.

The political power of the Sena family soon came into play. On August 10, 1912 President William Howard Taft commuted the sentence to read "con-currently" rather than "cumulatively," reducing imprisonment to a total of one year and one day.

Sena entered the New Mexico Penitentiary at Santa Fe on August 16, 1912. He was 52 years old and listed his occupation as "real estate." On January 25, 1913, President Taft commuted the sentence. Sena had served only five months and nine days. For all of his effort, he had gained nothing, but the effect on the ATC was devastating. During the trial little or no production had occurred as the company waited for the outcome, and most of its resources were allocated to legal expenses and to meeting the minimal assessment requirements. In spite of the favorable verdict, the company never recovered financially and never resumed full-scale mining operations.[42]

Mariano Sena, New Mexico State Records Center Archives, Santa Fe. New Mexico State Corrections Department Records negative number 3053.

Indigenous pueblos along the Rio Grande River, including Santo Domingo (now known as Kewa), Cochiti, and San Felipe, did not have the Euro-American concept of individual private ownership of the area's turquoise mines. They continued to exercise what they felt was their ancestral right to visit and gather turquoise for themselves and to sell to tourists and the shops in Albuquerque and Santa Fe.

When he was superintendent of the ATC mines on Turquoise Hill, J.P. McNulty often gave local Pueblo Indians poorer specimens and second-grade blue turquoise stones, but they preferred to do their own mining. Although the Tiffany mine was always off-limits, McNulty sometimes allowed them to work the Castilian. At times, small parties snuck into the mines at night, whereas other times they came well-armed and confrontational. More than once the Indians were hauled into the courts on trespass charges.[43]

On New Year's Eve, 1908, numerous Santo Domingos gathered around McNulty's house on Turquoise Hill and threatened to kill him while others entered the Tiffany to mine turquoise. Anthony Lovato, a respected jeweler of Tewa Pueblo (formerly Santo Domingo), relayed a story told by an elder of one of the raiders who was so laden with turquoise he could not make it back to the pueblo. He buried the stash under what he considered a recognizable tree, intending to return to reclaim the valuable hoard. He never found the tree.

On March 13, 1909, indictments for "entering a mine with intent to steal and malicious trespass" were filed, and warrants for Francisco Pacheco, Transito Romero, Manuel Tortolito, and Cruz Calabaza were issued. Sheriff Charles C. Clossen was able to locate, serve, and arrest Cruz Calabaza. He entered a plea of not guilty on April 17, 1909 to the charge of "entering a mine with intent to steal mineral." On the malicious trespass charge, Calabaza first entered a plea of not guilty then changed it to a plea of guilty, but the court withheld its sentence.

On September 13, 1910, four warrants were again issued in the case. This time Sheriff Clausen was unable to locate any of the accused. Finally on March 7, 1911, "Cause was dropped with leave to reinstate the motion" by the district attorney, but no further action was ever taken. Ironically, three days later, four Cochiti Pueblo men entered prison on charges of burglary of a different mine belonging to the ATC.

On the night of December 16, 1910, four men from nearby Cochiti Pueblo were captured while entering the Castilian mine. The warrant claimed they had "unlawfully, feloniously and burglariously entered the Castilian turquoise mine to take, steal and carry away turquoise, being the property of the ATC." On December 19, 1910 the *Santa Fe New Mexican* reported the following under the heading "Indian Turquoise Takers Are Not a Myth":

> The story of the removal of turquoise from the Tiffany mines by Indians who still feel they have a right to the semi-precious stones used in the ceremonies appears to be anything but a myth. For years J.P. McNulty, in charge of the mines, has been complaining that the Indians stole the turquoise by night, especially on moonlight nights, but it was an extremely difficult task to get proofs.

> There are now four Indians in the local jail brought hither yesterday morning by Deputy Sheriff Montoya of Cerrillos. A representative of the New Mexican interviewed one of the Indians this afternoon in jail. He, like his three companions of turquoise taking propensities, wore a red scarf around his black locks and held a lighted cigarette in his mouth. The red man punctuated his sentences with puffs from his cigarette. "My name it is Marcial Quintana," said the Indian. "I live at Cochiti. I go to Turquoise mines to get turquoise, that is true enough. We want

turquoise. Indians from Santo Domingo bring us turquoise to Cochiti, that is true enough, but they ask big price for it. We hear this mine was open and nobody watched it or care about it. We see sheriffs coming but not try to escape. We think we can get turquoise from mine which nobody watched."

The four appeared before Judge John R. McVie on burglary charges and were represented by special attorney for Pueblo Indians, F.C. Wilson, who waived formal arraignment in open court. All four entered pleas of guilty. The sentence was no less than six months or no more than nine months at hard labor in the New Mexico Penitentiary at Santa Fe. The four began their sentences on March 10 1911, and soon after Governor William Mills began to receive petitions calling for their release on parole. The charges were the first offenses for the four men and some felt sufficient punishment had been meted out to serve as a determent to further theft by these men or any other member of Cochiti Pueblo. Even sentencing Judge McVie wrote to the governor calling for a parole or pardon, stating, "They say that the Santo Domingo Indians who have been depredating these mines induced them to do it to screen themselves." On August 8, 1911, parole was approved and the men were allowed to return to their families.

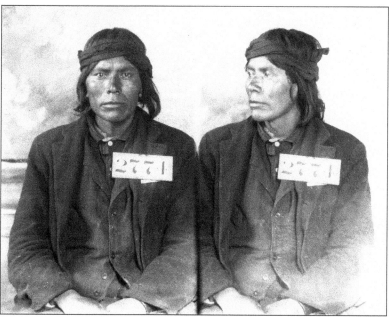

The Cochiti Four. New Mexico State Records Center Archives, Santa Fe. New Mexico State Corrections Department Records negative numbers 2771, 2772, 2773, 2775.

The ATC was not alone in its goal to capitalize on the increased demand and higher prices for turquoise. On April 11, 1892, Michael O'Neil and Ed F. Bennett staked the Persian Lode claim. It was in a promising location because it was bordered by the Old Castilian turquoise mine on the northwest and the Consul turquoise mine on the northeast, two mines that had been good producers.[44]

New Mexico Governor LeBaron Bradford Prince had become interested in the growing turquoise mining industry. Bennett wrote to him in a letter dated August 4, 1892:

> Your expressing a wish that you should like very much to be interested in some turquoise, and explaining conditions that have prevented you, leads me to remark that prospects of turquoise in this district are now nearly, or quite, all claimed; and though I've had the best of opportunities for owning such property there have been too many unfavorable conditions to mining, for some years, to allow my developing that sort of prospect. Still I'm interested in three such claims, and may someday operate them more profitably than means permit now. I am halves in the "Consul" and "Persian" on the southeast side of the "Old Castilian." If you fancy taking chances on such prospects perhaps these and the price might suit you as well as anything else now open to sale. I can combine these with the "Pasha" near there, if you wish that."[45]

It would appear a deal took place because on November 11, 1892, Bennett transferred his half interest in the "Persian" to his partner Michael O'Neil for "$1 and other considerations," who the next day transferred total interest in the "Persian" to Philip E. Moissin of New York City again for "$1 and other considerations." Governor Prince evidently was behind these transactions, setting the stage for a new business venture, because on March 29, 1893 O'Neil wrote to him: "I am working on the Bottom Dollar mine over in Hungry Gulch. I will be finished here the first of the month and will then commence work on the Persian turquoise claim."[46]

Soon after, on April 10, 1893, the Articles of Incorporation were filed in the office of the Secretary of the Territory of New Mexico and a meeting of the directors of the newly formed New Mexico Turquoise Company took place in Santa Fe. James W. Hess of Indianapolis, Indiana was elected president and

Governor Prince was elected to serve as secretary and treasurer. A motion was made and passed to buy the "Persian" claim for $500 worth of capital stock in the company (50 shares). On April 15, 1893 Governor Prince, acting as attorney to Moissin, transferred the claim and the New Mexico Turquoise Company was in business.

We may infer that Hess was made president either because he was a major investor or for his business experience, or both. Hess moved to Indianapolis in 1862 and started a dry goods business. He became involved in the Republican Party and was elected sheriff in 1882. Following a short time as a bridge contractor, he started the Indianapolis Lounge Company in 1884. A lounge is a one-piece recliner designed for one person and was an important fixture in Victorian drawing rooms. Indianapolis was the center of lounge manufacturing, with annual sales in excess of $1.5MM. In 1897, Senator Fairbanks appointed Hess postmaster, a position he held until his death in 1900. In his obituary there is no mention of his involvement in the New Mexico Turquoise Company, so it would appear this was not a major focus of his business activities.

On April 30, 1893, Governor Prince advised O'Neil to "Press on the work on the Persian as fast as you can. Get another man if you can use him to good effort. Go right on to amount of $150."[47] By May 6, O'Neil was working on the Persian and had found some small stones, but problems getting money from Story and Allen to pay his men for work on the Bottom Dollar mine was disruptive. Prince was in the East, and O'Neil requested an address to send the stones of any value recovered so far.

O'Neil completed this initial work on the claim the last day of May. As expected, the old location of the shaft had not produced very good results, and he shifted his efforts to a new place a little south of the original location with good results. Here he produced one pound and one ounce of good turquoise and a quantity of turquoise specimens of lesser quality. By June 18, O'Neil sent Prince a small blasting box of about 135 of the largest and finest stones he had found. Story had shown him a cigar box of his turquoise of similar size and color. These stones were most likely from the Tiffany mine of the ATC because it was McNulty's practice to send his turquoise in cigar boxes to Doty.

At this time, Governor Prince began a search for a lapidary to cut the rough stone and produce polished cabochons. Frederick J. Essig of Chicago replied to a query from Prince, expressing his interest in the work and stating he had "cut quite an amount" of New Mexico turquoise in the previous three years and was set up with the proper facilities to cut and process large quantities of rough material. His price for cutting ran from 15 to 20 cents per finished carat, depending on the nature of the stone. Prince also received a response from J.B. Paillard, a lapidary located at 80 Nassau Street in New York City, but he was unable to quote a price without first seeing the rough turquoise. He also said if a large quantity were to be processed, he would require additional equipment.

On August 4, 1893, M.W. Porterfield, a druggist from Silver City who was interested in the recent turquoise mining activity in Grant County, NM, wrote to Governor Prince from the Windsor European Hotel in Chicago:

> Dear Sir,
>
> I am here to see Mr. F.J. Essig who with others want to organize a company to handle a valuable turquoise property I have recently opened up near Silver City. They have knowledge of your discovery and are anxious to combine two in one organization claiming that each have points of merit that would be advantageous to a company if combined. My proposition to them was to put in one half interest of my property for $15,000 keeping the other half myself. They propose to form a stock company, 100,000 shares at $2.50 each par value and are arranging to place a few shares at $1.00 each among stone dealers here to secure their cooperation in marketing the product.
>
> If you can enter into a similar arrangement I can I think assist you somewhat in doing so. However I think Mr. Essig will write you on the subject. The plan would be, if we should combine the two to make it 200,000 shares instead of one, on the same terms as they make to me. To organize under the laws of the State of Illinois is not very expensive. The fee for the charter is $25 however since the first of July the whole expense would probably amount to $100.
>
> I will leave tomorrow to visit my parents for ten days. Please address me there. I will likely come back here before returning to New Mexico to look after this matter and would be glad to know your wish regarding the same before that time. My experience is that it is almost impossible for a man to get at the stone market except through the stone cutters and dealers and have decided after a thorough and expensive test to arrange it as stated.
>
> Hoping to hear from you,
> I am respectively
> M.W. Porterfield[48]

On August 15 the following letter was sent from Frederick J. Essig to Governor Prince:

Dear Sir,

I send the lot turquoise by express today. I find them a good quality and think you will find the best stone in going down. A Mr. Porterfield of Silver City has been here of late and I cut some stones of his, which also looks very promising. He tells me they have three claims between him and another man, Mr. Moore. We are about to promote a stock company and when I told Mr. Porterfield of your find we had an idea that we could combine the both, that is yours and Porterfield's into one company and cut and sell at the fair here to introduce the stones! The stone of Porterfield's comes in quite large and clear pieces but not quite blue enough although it is getting better as they go down.

Mr. Porterfield will also write you in regard to our plan. There are only two turquoise companies in America now and one more would be quite enough and by a combination of these two mines the market would be supplied with any shade and size which so ever is in demand in Europe and America.

Any more work you send will receive prompt attention.[49]

Hess, president of the company, wrote optimistically on August 17, 1893:

I am quite anxious to hear the report of the lapidary and hope these stones will show good color and take a good polish. If so I think we should push the work in the mine unless we can make a good sale.[50]

On September 27 Hess wrote to Prince in Chicago from Indianapolis:

I have your esteemed favor of recent date and have carefully considered the contents. I think your suggestions are good and believe we can in the way mentioned place some of our product on the market with good results. I have made arrangement to get a book which gives a complete list of all jewelers in the United States, should you wish me to do so. I can have the printing and mailing done here, you to furnish the manuscript. I am very anxious to see you and talk over matters, but while my health is much better than it has been for some time, I do not feel quite equal to encountering the crowd which I would have to meet in Chicago.[51]

Nothing came of these overtures to create a turquoise syndicate, but we see the seeds of future development that would unfold over the next several years, involving many of the same participants. When Hess received the list of American jewelers, he asked his friend J.B. Mayo, a cutter and dealer in New York City, to write to the ATC for a price list and any other information they might have on turquoise. Mayo had earlier corresponded with Prince, advising him that the best way to distribute the turquoise was to sell the rough to some leading jewelers for cutting and processing, adding that James Allen had reportedly sold $60,000 worth of rough to Tiffany a year ago.

It is not surprising that the response to Mayo's request from the ATC was less than enthusiastic, saying they needed to see any material before giving a price and referring him to E. Keressen and Company, which sent a card but no price list. This dialogue indicates that the New Mexico Turquoise Company lacked the same distribution network developed by the ATC and was trying, without much success, to duplicate through imitation, including staking their claim as close as possible to the Tiffany mine.

It was the promise of future riches that kept optimism and investment high, yet the reality did not meet the expectation. Keressen sent Prince some larger cut stones ranging from $5 to $14 per carat (about $100 to $300 in 2016 value) with a fair-sized stone priced about $30. These were enticing prospects, and when Prince returned to Santa Fe he sent a box of rough to M. Fox, who had worked with D.C. Hyde 12 years earlier and was one of the most respected cutters in the business. The results were disappointing, with unprofitable small stones and total carat weight. In addition, the turquoise O'Neil found had either too much matrix or was not the desired color to bring to market. Although there was a demand for small stones, the profit was in larger stones which, if the proper blue color, would bring as much as $14 to $20 per carat ($400 to $600 in current value).

Although Hess continued to be optimistic until his death in 1900, the New Mexico Turquoise Company was not financially successful. The company maintained the annual assessments on their claims, but little, if any, production took place, and Prince and others began to look elsewhere for turquoise and other mining opportunities. In 1907 the New Mexico Turquoise Company ceased all business.

Sometimes in our study of the past, we lose sight of the very human side of business. In 1904, in correspondence with Prince, Mary Hess, James' widow, wrote:

> The giving up of the mine gave me great pain as Mr. Hess and I believed the turquoise was there and if there had been money for me to risk I should have put more into it. There is no need to be grieved over it and I have put it from my mind. You write you have two stones you will send me as souvenirs of the mine. You are very kind and I shall be most glad to have them. I shall have them set and remember that once I was a mine owner. [52]

Mike O'Neil's Blue Bell and the Cerrillos Hills

Michael O'Neil played an important role in the story of Cerrillos during the years of The Great American Turquoise Rush. In addition to his involvement with the New Mexico Turquoise Company and operation of the Persian in Turquoise Hill, he worked countless other claims over the years, often closely and in friendly competition with James Patrick McNulty.

The Blue Bell claim was located on January 15, 1892 by O'Neil and Adam Herlich[53] on original American Indian workings in the Cerrillos Hills near the site of the old diggings on Mt. Chalchihuitl. Later that same year Herlich, transferred his half interest in the claim to O'Neil[54] in exchange for O'Neil's half interest in the Shah Claim on Turquoise Hill, closer to the claims of the ATC.[55] In 1894, O'Neil transferred one-half interest in both the Blue Bell and Last Chance Turquoise, both located on Turquoise Hill, to H.H. Topakyan of New York,[56] but evidently Topakyan never contributed to the annual $100 assessment work required by law because O'Neil published notices of foreclosure in the *Weekly Cerrillos Rustler* between January 29 and April 30 1897.[57] It is confusing because there are Blue Bell claims in the Cerrillos Hills and Turquoise Hill.

H.H. Topakyan, born to an established Armenian family in 1864 in the Ottoman Empire, became a rug merchant in Istanbul before immigrating to the United States in 1884 and becoming a U.S. citizen. With a flair for publicity and success in his rug business ,he came to the notice of the Shah of Iran and served as Persia's commissioner general at the World Columbian Exposition (Chicago, 1893), combining public diplomacy with his business interest of marketing Persian rugs. He was Persia's consul general in New York during and after World War I, and he spoke out against the Armenian genocide. Topakyan died in 1926, plunging from a 17th story window of the Yale Club, opposite Madison Square Garden, in what police concluded was an accidental fall.

H.H. Topakyan. Photo Library of Congress, Bain Collection. Public domain.

Looking northwest along Blue Bell turquoise claim, four miles north of Cerrillos. D.B. Sterrett, *U.S. Geological Survey*, 397.

Open cut and shaft on Blue Bell. D.B. Sterrett, *U.S. Geological Survey*, 398.

On August 25, 1897, O'Neil regained sole ownership of the Blue Bell[58] in the Cerrillos Hills and transferred one-fourth interest to his business associate in the New Mexico Turquoise Company, L. Bradford Prince, for $25,000.[59] This was a significant price and indicates the high hopes Prince had for this claim. Later, in 1902, Prince acquired the remaining three-quarter interest,[60] and the claim was patented in his name in 1906. It was the only turquoise claim to be patented in the Cerrillos Hills. At some point before 1911, O'Neil reacquired the claim. In 1911, when visited by D.B. Sterrett of the USGS, it was referred to simply as the Mike O'Neil turquoise mine. Upon O'Neil's death in 1930, the property passed to his grandson Vern Byrne.

The Quest for a Cartel

A monopoly is defined as having control of the supply or trade in a commodity or service. A cartel is an association of suppliers whose purpose is to maintain high prices and restrict competition. During The Great American Turquoise Rush, several companies and claim owners tried to establish a monopoly to control supply and distribution of turquoise. We have seen how Porterfield attempted to combine the New Mexico Turquoise Company and their Persian claim with his claims in the Burro Mountains in Grant County, New Mexico. The spirit of the age—to establish economic domination—transpired before antitrust legislation forced the oil, steel, and financial monopolies to split apart. Although the turquoise industry was relatively small when compared with the wealth of other commodities and industries, intense competition for control developed.

The pattern was similar in the different areas where turquoise was mined. Local prospectors and miners discovered the mines, usually on sites of previous ancient Indian mining activity, and located a claim. This attracted the attention of local businessmen, who would buy the claim and acquire it through deed. These entrepreneurs then strove to attract investment capital from the major financial and retail centers of New York and Chicago. This was the case with the ATC and was the model the New Mexico Turquoise Company adopted.

As we have seen, the New Mexico Turquoise Company struggled to keep up with expenses for operating the mine and paying for annual assessments to keep the Persian claim current. In a letter dated Dec 6, 1899, six months before his death, James Hess wrote to his fellow shareholders in an attempt to raise contributions for the annual $100 assessment fee to keep the claim active. He related how he and Prince had struggled for three years to keep the mine open and had together invested $1,700. He spoke highly of the prospects, and in conversations with J.P. McNulty, stated he was advised to cut to intercept a vein from the Old Castilian mine adjacent to the Persian. He added that McNulty claimed the Old Castilian had paid Tiffany $2MM since 1892.[61]

In correspondence dated December 29, Hess mentioned the land grant dispute and the entrance of a new investor in the NMTC, William Taylor, attorney general of Indiana:

> If we can make the arrangements to get into a syndicate and get our property in at a fair value in stock, I will be willing that such arrangements be made. You and I hold a controlling interest in the stock, consequently, can do what we think for the best interest of all concerned.[62]

In February, Prince received a letter from the New Jersey Corporations Agency informing him he had been elected a director of the North American Turquoise Syndicate that had been formed in November of 1899.[63] He was issued a stock certificate for 100 shares in the company in May. The managing director of the syndicate was A. McGregor Leffingwell, an investment banker from New Haven, Connecticut. He had assembled a reputable list of directors for the company including former governors of New Mexico Territory, William T. Thornton and L. Bradford Prince. General George H. Ford, a well-known jeweler from New Haven, was presumably going to assist with distribution. In a letter on ATC letterhead dated April 26, 1900 to Edward Bartlett, lead attorney for the ATC in the land grant case, Robert Parker, who had taken over the management of the company representing the bondholders after the foreclosure in 1897 made the following observations:

> The ruling spirit in this syndicate is one A. McGregor Leffingwell, who interviewed me some months ago with a view to getting an option on our property. I investigated the man. I do not think he has any capital of his own, and he did not impress me favorably at all. He hailed originally from New Haven, Conn. But has for some time lived in Chicago. He is a sort of "free lance." By the way, how are our titles at the present time on the Santa Fe and Grant County properties? Leffingwell pretended that he knew they were defective, and his statement to that effect conveyed a somewhat veiled threat. [64]

Leffingwell appeared to be of dubious character, if not an outright con man. In the October 18, 1899 edition of *The Jewelers Circular,* a leading trade publication, an article reported that several leading jewelers, including Moses Kahn of the Azure Mining Company, J.G. Doty of the ATC, and Charles F. Wood, had been approached with the idea of joining a syndicate, with no indication of interest and with the general consensus that such an effort to form a trust would not be successful. Yet according to the Circular article, Leffingwell claimed in an interview with a staff reporter that the proposed turquoise combination was under way, that it would take definite form during the week, and that he had options on nearly all the mines in New Mexico except for those of the Azure and American Turquoise companies. He further claimed they would have offices in New York, Boston, Paris, Antwerp, and Amsterdam with the idea of doing with turquoise what De Beers Consolidated Mines Co. had done with diamonds. His goal, he said, was to bring all the mines together but if that were not possible to be large enough to "force a general co-operation in regard to prices and methods even if there be no consolidation of interests."[65] Evidently the decidedly cavalier attitude of Leffingwell in bragging about relationships with established turquoise companies that appeared to be entirely fabrications was not well received by those companies, as was apparent in the following posting from a December issue of *The Jeweler's Circular:*

> Tiffany and Co has denounced unauthorized and absolutely untrue reports in newspapers associating their name with the management of the North American Turquoise Syndicate. Tiffany and Co has nothing to do with the concern and object to use of their name in connection with it. [66]

There is no indication that the North American Turquoise Syndicate was successful with any of these ambitions and indeed never acquired any claims. During the period Prince was serving on the board of the syndicate and was a shareholder, he was actively pursuing the retention of the Persian claim for the NMTC and working closely with the successor investors to James Hess, William Taylor, Mary Hess, and Austin Quick, who presumably succeeded Hess at the Indianapolis Lounge Company. Leffingwell wrote to Prince hoping he had been successful in "capturing Turquoise Mountain for the North American Turquoise Syndicate." Perhaps this was a reference to Turquoise Hill, but the ATC, which clearly had indicated no interest in working with Leffingwell, primarily held those claims. [67]

L. Bradford Prince North American Turquoise Syndicate stock certificate. New Mexico State Records Center and Archives.

In a letter dated November 28 to Prince, who was in transit to New York for a board meeting of the North American Turquoise Syndicate, Quick mentioned:

> I saw Mr. Taylor today and he is very anxious to have you visit Indianapolis and thought you might do so on your way to New York. Mr. Taylor thinks that we should have an election of officers. I do not think it would be difficult to get $4000 or $5000 to put in the turquoise mine and Mr. Taylor seems to think so.

While Prince was in New York, Quick wrote:

> Mr. Taylor is worth considerable money and is much interested in the mining region of N.M. Taylor has a great many wealthy friends. I talked to [Taylor] about raising $5,000 for the turquoise mine and he seemed very favorable.[68]

The investors proved elusive, but on December 14, 1900, Taylor sent $100 to Prince "for work on our turquoise mine to pay Michael O'Neil of Cerrillos, whom I understand you have employed to do the work."

LeBaron Bradford Prince, governor of New Mexico Territory 1889-1893, ca. 1890. Courtesy of Palace of Governors Photo Archives (NMHM/DCA), negative number 050444.

These events offer insights into the turquoise mining industry of the 1890s. Reported production numbers were often suspect. Reason demanded the lack of trust in a business based upon the complex interaction of claims that required annual investment and registration to be valid. When Hess touted McNulty's production numbers from the Old Castilian, either Hess misunderstood and the numbers were total ATC production for the period, almost exclusively from the Tiffany mine, or McNulty was purposely misleading Hess, who had little mining experience. The Old Castilian had produced for Story and Allen when they worked it prior to selling to the ATC in 1892. According to Milford, the ATC instructed McNulty not to allow any visitors on the property and to keep production a secret.

Prince's activities indicate it was not uncommon for an investor to have several prospects in place, perhaps playing one against the other. Mining is a speculative venture, and the chances of success with investors increased with the number of possibilities. In the case of the North American Turquoise Syndicate, though it appears Leffingwell was trying to exploit Prince, quite the opposite was taking place. The attempts in the Cerrillos area to create a dominant presence in the turquoise trade were happening at the same time as major efforts affecting The Great American Turquoise Rush were transpiring in the Burro Mountains of Grant County, New Mexico.

Perhaps the most enduring legacy of those companies operating in Cerrillos was that of the ATC in forever associating the Tiffany brand with both the area and a host of other turquoise mines throughout the West that attempted to exploit the name even though no connection existed. Tiffany and Co. was certainly the principal, if not the exclusive, buyer of the turquoise produced by the ATC, primarily from the Tiffany (Muñiz) mine, because of John Andrews's relationship as a former employee and shareholder of the firm. We know the ATC sold to and had investment from other jewelers, including William Alling, yet none had the prestige or reputation of Tiffany. It is the Tiffany name that endures in the imagination of turquoise lovers, long after other participants have been forgotten.

Notes

1. Lewis B. Lesley, ed., *Uncle Sam's Camels,* Huntington Library Press, 2006, vi.
2. W.P. Blake, "W.P. Blake on the Chalchihuitl of the Mexicans," *American Journal of Science,* vol. 25, 1858.
3. William B. Carter, *Indian Alliances and the Spanish in the Southwest, 750–1750,* 145–146.
4. Carter, 90.
5. W.P. Blake, 1858, 229.
6. Homer Milford, New Mexico Abandoned Mine Land Bureau, Reports 1994-1, 20–21.
7. S.E. Wallace, *The Land of the Pueblo,* 1888, 87–88.
8. F. Jones, "Economic Geology of New Mexico," *U.S. Geological Survey,* 1908.
9. *Weekly New Mexican,* April 12, 1879.
10. *Santa Fe Daily New Mexican,* July 7, 1880.
11. Homer Milford, New Mexico Abandoned Mine Land Bureau, Reports 1994-1.
12. W.P. Blake, 1858, 229.
13. Hyde, n.d., 4 and 10.
14. Ibid.
15. Hyde n.d., 9 and 10.
16. Milford, Report 1994-1, 19.
17. Hyde, n.d., 11.
18. Milford, Report 1994-1, 19–20.
19. Milford, Report 1994-1, 20.
20. Ibid.
21. G.F. Kunz, *Mineral Resources of the United States, 1883,* 495.
21. H. Milford, *History of Cerrillos Turquoise Mining,* (Santa Fe: Cultural Resource Survey of Turquoise Hill, 1995, 30.
23. G.F. Kunz, *Mineral Resources of the United States, 1893,* 763.
24. A. Khazeni, *Sky Blue Stone, The Turquoise Trade in World History,* 121.
25. Joseph E. Pogue, *The Turquois: Memoirs Of The National Academy Of Science* (Glorieta, NM: National Academy of Sciences, 1915), 135.
26. Sena vs. ATC 1907 trial testimony, 134, 138.
27. *New York Tribune,* July 13, 1865.
28. Milford, 44.
29. Milford, 42–43.
30. J. Batkin, *The Native American Curio Trade in New Mexico* (Wheelwright Museum of the American Indian, 2015), 58.
31. Santa Fe New Mexican cited in *The Cerrillos Rustler,* vol. iii, no.47. May 29, 1891.
32. W. Baxter, *High Desert News,* Fall 2011.
33. Patricia McCraw, *Tiffany Blue* Santa Fe: 2006, 26.
34. Obituary, *New York Times,* March 10, 1894.
35. Comments on Arizona Historical Society documents.
36. *New York Times,* February 7, 1894.
37. McCraw, *Tiffany Blue,* 5.
38. McCraw, *Tiffany Blue,* 8.
39. M.O. Murphy, "Turquoise In The Cerrillos Hills," *Lapidary Journal,* no. 14, 1962, 738.
40. McCraw, *Tiffany Blue,* 19.
41. McCraw, *Tiffany Blue,* 327–321.
42. McCraw, *Tiffany Blue,* 236.
43. Homer Milford, 46–47.

44. Prince papers, New Mexico State Records and Archives.
45. Ibid.
46. Ibid.
47. Ibid.
48. Ibid.
49. Ibid.
50. Ibid.
51. Ibid.
52. Ibid.
53. Santa Fe County Mining Records Book 2, 259–260.
54. Santa Fe County Mining Deeds Book J, , 39–40.
55. Ibid., 40–41.
56. Ibid., 188–189.
57. Santa Fe County Records of Location and Mining Deeds, Book K, 90.
58. Ibid.
59. Ibid. 328.
60. Santa Fe County Mining Quick Claim Deeds Book F-1,.
61. Prince Papers, Hess letter December 6, 1899.
62. Prince Papers, Hess letter dated December 29, 1899.
63. Ibid., letter dated February, 8, 1900.
64. Prince Papers, correspondence dated April 26, 1900.
65. *The Jewelers Circular,* October 18, 1899, 23–24.
66. *The Jewelers Circular and Horological Review,* December 6, 1899, 29.
67. Prince Papers, letter dated September 13, 1900.
68. Prince Papers, letters dated November and December 1900.

3

Burro Mountains (Tyrone)

Rediscovery of the Old Mines

At the same time the ATC was first starting operations in the Turquoise Hills of Cerrillos, others were busy with competing efforts in Grant County, New Mexico, near the town of Silver City. In many ways these companies would surpass the quantity and the quality of turquoise coming from Cerrillos.

The Mimbreno Apache Indian branch of the Mogollon Culture, A.D. 850–1350 were reported to have mined turquoise in the Burro Mountains. During the 1870s, settlers came across these mines, however, events surrounding the discovery will probably never be known. Contemporary accounts and newspaper articles of the times are sketchy at best, indicating the original discoverers were unaware at the time of the importance of their findings.

Early accounts credit brothers Robert and John Metcalf with the initial discovery of the old turquoise and copper workings in 1871, but hostilities with native Apaches prevented any mineral development in the area at that time. John E. Coleman, aka "Turquoise John," a veteran of the California Gold Rush of 1848–1855, is most often given credit for finding the earlier American Indian turquoise mines in the Burros while on a hunting trip in the mid- to late-1870s.[1] This belief may be based upon accounts that Coleman filed the "Calaite" claim at that time and sold it to T.S. Parker and M.W. Porterfield in 1882. Fayette Jones stated this in 1904, and it was repeated by John Cowen in 1911. In fact, the Calaite claim was not located and recorded until 1890. M.W. Porterfield had arrived in Silver City in 1888 following his brother W.C. who had arrived from Illinois in 1887 and had established the Porterfield Drug Company. The myth of Turquoise John was well known and is demonstrated by this 1948 account from *New Mexico Magazine*:

In that long ago year, 1875, John Coleman had cautiously worked his way through the dense growth of pinon, juniper and oak which grew on the slopes of the Burro Mountains to the west of St. Louis Canyon. A jay called raucously. The little bearded man frowned. That noisy alarm could serve equally well to warn the deer that might be bedded down around the next point or to warn a lurking Apache assassin. Stopping in a thick clump of scrub oak John stood motionless for many minutes as his eyes searched out every part of the mountainside, studied every clump of timber. At last satisfied that no danger lurked in the near vicinity, John resumed his silent stalk through the timber, seeking a deer to replenish the larder at his camp up the canyon. Starting down the side of a shallow canyon, he was struck by the appearance of a low grass-grown mound over which he had stumbled. A spot of color caught his eye. Stooping he picked up a small piece of red pottery, looked at it idly and tossed it aside. Potsherds held no attraction for him. He was about to walk on when he noticed a peculiarly shaped stone at the edge of the heap. It was a perfectly formed stone axe, obviously of Indian workmanship and obviously very, very old. A gleam of interest lighted his eyes as he examined it. "These must be old Indian diggin's," he muttered, "what'd they be diggin for—gold?" Excitement gripped John as he leaned his rifle against a nearby tree and knelt to scrape in the mound with the stone axe. A glint of blue caught his eye. "Turquoise!" he exclaimed as he examined the bit of blue stone.[2]

"Turquoise" John Coleman. Courtesy of Palace of Governors Photo Archives (NMHM/DCA), negative number 174556.

Another person credited as an early discoverer was William J. Foley of Silver City. In an article by Charles H. Snow from 1891 in the *American Journal of Science,* Foley is reported to have received a letter from a firm of Indian traders stating the Navajos claimed ancient turquoise mine workings occurred near Silver City.[3] The contents of the letter and Coleman's discovery of the old turquoise mines in the area years before may have persuaded Coleman and Foley to team up. The Calaite claim was located in both of the men's names on November 15, 1890.[4] It is interesting that when naming the claim, Coleman and Foley reference the name *callais* for turquoise, which comes from *Pliny's Natural History,* first published in A.D. 77. Since the claim filing predates mention of this by Fayette Jones in *New Mexico Mines and Minerals in 1904,* and a more detailed account by Pogue in 1915, we might imagine these two prospectors had some experience with the classics.

When Snow first visited the site, he found ancient excavations scattered over several adjoining hillsides. Although they extended over a wide area, the workings occurred in small, isolated groups with no signs of systematic development. The size and character of the waste rock piles indicated that most of the workings had been shallow, though at one time at least one deep pit existed. One hillside showed signs that ancient miners had driven a tunnel, but almost all evidence of prehistoric adits and pits were obliterated. Well-established vegetation concealed piles—some quite large—of waste rock, and debris from ancient mining verified signs of excavation by primitive technology. The country rock consisted of gray quartz with white cleavable feldspar containing small pieces of turquoise still adhering to some of the host.[5]

After filing the Calaite claim, Foley, in partnership with veteran miner Nicholas C. Rascom, located, on December 3, 1890, a second claim about a mile away near the "Chief of the Burros" copper mine, which they named the "Persian".[6] This site originally had been a small, one-cubic-yard test pit in which the turquoise veins had evidently been mistaken as shavings for copper. It was located on the summit of a buff-colored dike, and contained a perfect network of turquoise that ranged in thickness from one eighth of an inch or less. Often the thicker material forked into multiple thinner ones, and these subdivided again into even smaller ones. The thicker material could be separated from the host rock at its point of contact. In some places, small dots of turquoise, a deeper blue than the standard vein material, occurred within isolated areas.

Less than seven months after its discovery, Foley transferred a one-twelfth interest in the Persian to Florence E. Dorsey, and at the same time Foley and Coleman transferred an undetermined interest in the Calaite to her.[7] Evidently something happened—perhaps the assessment work was not performed or recorded—because on New Year's Day 1892, Foley, in partnership with J.D. Smith of Grant County, relocated the Persian.[8] J.D. Smith sold his half interest in the mine five months later to Wesley S. Block of Kings County, New York for $1,000.[9] Block filed an affidavit of assessment for the Persian in 1893, and Foley also filed an assessment notice for the Persian at the same time as his annual filing for the Calaite as well as keeping up the filing in 1894. Wesley Block, with his brother John, was also involved in other turquoise mining activities. The brothers were diamond merchants located at 9 Maiden Lane, New York City. Their involvement indicated the extensive level of interest in the turquoise market in the Southwest from the New York jeweler community. They are an example of many such participants in The Great American Turquoise Rush who worked with the major players but never quite reached the top level.

The Azure Mining Company

The largest shareholder and founder of the Azure Mining Company was Gyulo Armeny. Born in Hungary in 1850, Armeny immigrated to the United States at the age of 19. He married and found work at a jeweler's bench in the Bronx, where he learned the trade. After some years, he was successful enough to begin his own jewelry manufacturing business in the Bronx. He moved on to employment with John A. Riley, a preeminent New York jeweler, and soon after founded his business at 75 Nassau Street in the center of the jewelry district. While still involved in this business, he entered into partnership in 1887 with William C. Marion, a veteran in the manufacture of gold fountain pens, and they set up shop as Armeny and Marion at 100 Maiden Lane.

Business evidently prospered, and in 1890 they moved to anchor a building at the corner of Nassau and Fulton built by Frank Raub, a real estate developer and saloon owner. In 1893, Armeny purchased the property and it continues to be known as the Armeny Building. An obituary from the preeminent trade publication of the time, *The Jewelers' Circular,* dated April 14, 1920, stated that shortly after entering the pen business, Armeny was less active in the manufacture of jewelry. Up to the time of his death, however, he always wanted to be known as a jeweler as well as a pen maker. The piece also mentioned that Armeny was an expert in precious and semi-precious stones and owned mining operations in New Mexico and South America.

Julius Lippman Tannenbaum figures prominently throughout The Great American Turquoise Rush. His tale is no less interesting than that of Armeny, although not without a bit of tarnish. Tannenbaum was born in Germany in 1851 and immigrated to the United States in 1868. His early years were less than distinguished. A report from the *New York Times* in March 1877 noted: "Another of the somewhat notorious Tannenbaum family was arrested on a bench warrant yesterday on a charge of obtaining goods by false premises." The article stated that Tannenbaum and his brother Nathan allegedly misrepresented themselves as heirs to Nathan's deceased wife and used her net worth as collateral for obtaining $700 worth of jewelry. In addition, Nathan had since left the city with as much as $40,000 in stolen property. Lippman Tannenbaum was arrested but presumably found not guilty. Later that same year he founded L. Tannenbaum and Company, a diamond importing and cutting firm.

Evidently Armeny and Tannenbaum were well acquainted—both had offices on Nassau Street, Tannenbaum at 65 and Armeny at 75. They must have shared an interest in colored gemstones because in June of 1891, they partnered to lease the mine of the Emerald and Hiddenite Mining Company, and paid William E. Hidden, the owner of the mine and hiddenite discoverer, an annual rental of $1,000 plus 10 percent of the net profits. At this time, according to Tannenbaum, he and Armeny made a verbal agreement that should either of them enter into any other mining operations, they would remain partners.

Armeny was evidently pursuing the ownership of turquoise mining claims in the Burro Mountains at this time. Shortly after forming his business venture with Tannenbaum, he purchased several claims and promptly signed them over to the newly formed Azure Mining Company. The sequence of these claims provides insight to several key participants in the turquoise trade.

After the initial staking activities of Coleman and Foley at the Calaite, Rascom, along with George A. Cox, located two more claims, the Jewel and Turquoise Mine on January 5, 1891. The Jewel was described as lying parallel and on the western side of the Calaite with the location monument situated 500 feet in a northwesterly direction from the ancient workings on the Calaite, and 400 yards in an easterly direction from the trail that ran from Pascal to Bald Mountain.[10] The Turquoise Mine was described as being 1.1 miles in a northeasterly direction from Pascal Trail. Less than three months later Cox sold his half interest to Porterfield for $50,[11] making Porterfield and Rascom equal partners.

A little over five weeks later, Rascom and Porterfield located two more claims. The Emerald was located on February 13, 1891 on the east side of St. Louis Gulch and about one mile below the St. Louis mine. The location monument was about 500 feet southeast of the southeast corner of the Burro Chief.

The next day, Valentine's Day, they located the Santa Fe Claim described as about 1.5 miles northeast from Pascal with the location monument erected at the northwest corner of the Gem.

At this point, Armeny entered the picture. Nine weeks after locating the Santa Fe and Emerald, on April 20, 1891, three additional claims were located. The Azure was about one mile northeast of Pascal with its west end center monument 20 feet north of the Pascal-Bald Mountain Trail. The Cabinet was about 1,000 yards south of Cane Spring, on the ridge running from Pascal to Mangus Canyon. The third, the Arthur, was located 1.5 miles from Pascal with its monument 900 feet west of the ancient workings on the Calaite claim. Eight days after these claims were located, the Gem was found on the northern side of the Turquoise Mine claim. In May, four more claims were located: the Henry Clay, Blue Bell, Ruby, and Diadem.

On August 11, 1891, Rascom deeded his half interest in the Santa Fe, Emerald, Jewell, and Turquoise claims to Gyulo Armeny. The first was made solely by Rascom to Armeny and recorded in the amount of $4,000.[12] A second deed recorded October 26, 1891 included Rascom's wife plus an additional $1,000. This deed was recorded the same day that Armeny transferred all 14 of the claims he had acquired from Rascom and Porterfield, and those he had located himself, to the newly formed Azure Mining Company, which had incorporated October 9, 1891.

The addition of Rascom's wife and the additional payment indicates that Armeny, aware of trouble brewing in Rascom's marriage, desired the security of a clear, uncontestable title to the properties, even at extra expense. This proved a wise move. The Rascoms divorced and the Santa Fe claim produced millions of dollars' worth of turquoise over the next few years.

Only days later, on August 15, 1891, Porterfield transferred the half interest he had claimed with Rascom in the Santa Fe and Emerald claims, the half interest purchased from George Cox in the Jewell and Turquoise claims, and the half interest he had claimed with Armeny the Gem, Henry Clay, Pearl, Arthur, Malachite, Azure, Cabinet, Deadem, Ruby, and Blue Bell to Armeny for a total price of $14,000.[13]

As Armeny was putting together this assortment of claims for his new turquoise venture, he approached his partner Tannenbaum with the opportunity to invest in the project. Tannenbaum declined because he felt the quality of the sample turquoise Armeny showed him was inferior. Armeny then approached some of his New York jewelry trade colleagues to invest, and they formed a corporation, The Azure Mining Company. The mines were successful and in 1892, Tannenbaum went back to Armeny claiming he had been cheated and Armeny had intentionally shown him low-quality samples. He filed a lawsuit that reached the New York Supreme Court, which determined Tannenbaum was due part of the gains Armeny made from the sale of the Azure mine to the Azure Mining Company. There is reference to an accounting to be made to determine this value, which is understandable because the deed dated 10/19/1891 shows Armeny transferred the title to the Azure Mining Company of 14 claims—Santa Fe, Emerald, Jewel, Turquoise, Gem, Henry Clay, Pearl, Arthur, Malachite, Azure, Cabinet, Deadem, Ruby and Blue Bell—for consideration of $1. Armeny had paid thousands for the claims and had not benefitted economically from the sale.

The accommodation Armeny made to settle the judgment must not have satisfied Tannenbaum, who reportedly flew into "spasms of rage" whenever Armeny and the lawsuit was mentioned.[14] In a later chapter we will discover a possible explanation of this "accounting." Both Tannenbaum and Armeny would be involved in a lawsuit with W.E. Hidden over a dispute regarding the Emerald and Hiddenite Mine in North Carolina they leased from Hidden. Hidden also made forays into the New Mexico turquoise market with one documented journey into the Jarilla Hills.

Evidently the reference to the accounting to be made by Armeny to Tannenbaum included claims because Jacobson reported:

> The Himalaya Mining Company turquoise mine, near Silver City, Grant County, New Mexico was opened circa 1901 near the Azure mine. Locating this claim near the Azure mine may reflect Tannenbaum's hope that "if I can't share in owning the largest turquoise mine, maybe another mine nearby will be just as valuable."[15]

The authors have been unable to verify that Tannenbaum did in fact own a turquoise mine in this area, although it may have been in the name of an associate of his. The Himalaya Mining Company was not formed until 1901, when Tanenbaum became involved in a tourmaline mine in California. This may have been confused with the turquoise mining Tannenbaum undertook in Courtland, Arizona.

The Azure Mining Company was incorporated under the laws of the State of New York on October 9, 1891 for the "operation of turquoise mines and the mining, cutting, and selling of the products thereof." This was four months before ATC filed for incorporation. The company was capitalized at

$2,000, consisting of 400 shares of a par value of $5. The shareholders were Gyulo Armeny (200 shares), Louis Kahn (34 shares), and President Moses Kahn (33 shares), Samuel H. Levy (33 shares), and Secretary Meyer D. Rothschild (100 shares). A significant and important difference in the means of how the two companies were financed was that while the ATC immediately borrowed $250,000 in bonds for working capital, the Azure Mining Company appeared to have been financed from the start solely with equity investment from the shareholders. This explains the different levels of financial stability the two companies experienced over the next several years, despite both being extremely successful in finding and selling turquoise.

L & M Kahn & Co. was a respected importer and wholesale dealer of watches, jewelry, precious and semi-precious stones, as well as diamonds, which had been in business since the early 1860s. Meyer D. Rothschild had worked for them for 12 years before taking over part of their business when he became president of the American Gem and Pearl Company in 1903. Rothschild, whose younger brother Alonzo was a co-publisher and owner of *The Jewelers' Circular,* also succeeded Louis Kahn as president of the Azure Mining Company. These three men were held in high regard by the New York jewelry trade, and were considered as well-known as Tiffany.[16] With this team in place, Armeny succeeded in securing a potential source for turquoise and would serve as general manager of those mines. His partners were men who could process and sell the finished product and were well versed in how to market it in the retail sector. Perhaps most importantly he had obtained investors who were well capitalized, and the Azure Mining Company would not be subject to the same financial difficulties as the ATC.

The Azure Mine and the Elizabeth Pocket

The Azure Mining Company commenced turquoise mining operations in late 1891 and continued to produce significant amounts of turquoise until 1905 or so. Production slowed after that, and by 1910 there was no more output. Over that time, the company owned as many as 40 claims and continued its existence for many years. As late as 1924, Louis Kahn was still registered as president and Meyer Rothschild as secretary. By that time attention in the Burros had shifted from turquoise to copper exploration. Edward Turner was the first registered agent of the company and served from 1891–1901. The first superintendent was Felix Vogel who oversaw the development of what proved to be the most productive and profitable turquoise mine of the era.

From the first, the mine operated at a steady rate of production, although the revenue produced barely paid expenses. The company had been making regular shipments for the six months prior to July 1892.[17] In September of 1892, four men were employed and the quality was described as superior.[18] George Kuntz reported that for 1892, the combined sales of Cerrillos and Burro Mountains exceeded $100,000.[19] The success and character of the Azure Mining Company was determined in large part by Felix Vogel's discovery in 1893 of what became known as the Elizabeth Pocket in an area of the Azure zone. Located at the southwest end of the open cut, this area produced more high-grade turquoise than had ever been discovered to that point in U.S. recorded history.

The chemical composition of turquoise is $CuAl_6 (PO_4)_4(OH)_8 \bullet 4H_2O$. It is a hydrous basic copper aluminum phosphate. In this area the phosphoric acid necessary for turquoise formation was probably derived from the decomposition of apatite within the granite, while the alumina was supplied by the decomposition of feldspar within the same rock.[20] Turquoise in nugget form is found where feldspar in the rock was most extensively kaolinized, whereas hard-vein turquoise is found in less altered rock. In more moderately altered rock both varieties were found.[21] For a stone to achieve the best color of blue and a desirable hardness, to protect from color alteration with use, the proper percentage of copper was very important. An excessive proportion would cause the color to tend toward green, whereas an insufficient quantity resulted in turquoise of pale color and inadequate hardness. The character of the turquoise varied often along the Azure vein. A light greenish-blue might be bisected by a much bluer one making it evident that the two different formations were deposited at different times and under different conditions and that there had been movement and fracturing of the host rock.[22] Turquoise formed when copper-bearing solutions rising in fissures with a northwest dip intersected fissures containing phosphate-bearing solutions with a southeast dip.

This area became known as the Azure mine and was developed on the Santa Fe and Gem claims, according to Rogge and Shepard.[23] A camp including a superintendent's home, office, sorting house, water storage facility, workshops for carpentry and machine work, and a blacksmith was established with adobe and frame houses for the workers. The color was mostly a deep blue, slightly translucent, and with hardness above 6 on the Mohs Hardness Scale, making it an ideal gemstone for jewelry. The turquoise occurred as both vein material filling cracks in the altered granite, and as nuggets embedded in kaolin. As much as 22 pounds of extremely high-grade material, mostly in nugget form, was produced within one month.

At first the turquoise was obtained from underground workings, but the material was so thoroughly distributed that soon workers drove an open cut the entire length of the vein. This single pocket, occurring near the surface, measured 150 feet long, 40 feet wide, and 50 feet deep. Early work was done through four adits driven northeast from Azure Canyon. This furnished a good dumping ground and made hoisting equipment unnecessary. Most of the good turquoise occurred near the surface, so much of the mine was converted to open cut. Underground development was done in advance to determine character and quality. The face of the cut was advanced 50–80 feet per year and eventually what became known as the "Santa Fe" cut was 1,000 feet long by 60 feet wide at the bottom of the pit, 150 feet wide at the top, and 75 deep. In its day, it was the largest turquoise mine in the world.

The vein rock near the Elizabeth Pocket was of a medium-fine- to course-grained structure, and was crossed by a large quantity of quartz veins, some more than a half inch thick. At other times, small quartz crystals penetrated the vein turquoise from the sides of the vein bordered by bands of kaolinized feldspar. At times, the quartz gave way to bright blue turquoise partly or completely filling the vein or as isolated specks within the quartz. Often the turquoise vein was isolated from the granite by quartz on one or both sides, and at other times the turquoise was found in direct contact with the host rock without any associated quartz. The turquoise that did occur mixed with the quartz was usually evenly grained and light blue.[24] The quantity and quality of turquoise produced from the Elizabeth Pocket created an abundance of riches because to place that amount of turquoise on the market at one time would have depressed prices. The Azure Mining Company had the enviable luxury of stockpiling turquoise to organize distribution to maximize profits. This situation was another reason turquoise companies maintained such secrecy concerning their operations.

In mining the turquoise, four car tracks were used. Before blasting, these were covered with logs, and after the bench shot the tracks were cleared and the rock shoved into the cars. At this point, the turquoise was picked out and put into buckets. A slight downhill grade to the dump overlooking Azure Canyon permitted gravity to contribute to waste rock removal. Either sledgehammers or light explosives broke up coarse rock. When loading finer rock, special care was taken to avoid any loss of turquoise. Often two men watched what went into the ore cars while the dirt was raked and the turquoise picked out. On good days two or three buckets might be recovered.

Elizabeth Pocket at the Azure mine. L.C. Grafton, *U.S. Geological Survey*, 1905, 59.

Blast at the Azure mine. L.C. Grafton, *U.S. Geological Survey*, 1905, 60.

Once the turquoise had been removed from the ground, it was moved to the sorting house, which was located near the superintendent's house. A uniform, un-tinted light was needed to differentiate the many shades and gradations of color. For this reason, the sorting house ceiling was covered with white cheesecloth and white shades covered the four windows to cast good light on the white oilcloth-covered sorting tables. First the buckets of turquoise were brought from the mine and emptied into boxes that were numbered and dated. The sorting was done on the tables under the watchful eye of the superintendent, who usually performed the first sort for the highest-grade material. The rest was then passed to the sorters for further classification. Although some poached turquoise found its way to Silver City, almost all of that came from mine workers. The mostly Hispanic employees within the sorting house were honored with complete trust and little, if any, turquoise was ever taken.

For turquoise to be graded first-class, both vein material and nuggets were flawless and of good color and quality. Second-class was any blue stone worth shipping plus any turquoise with matrix. Excessive host rock was removed using special cutting pliers and sorting hammers on small iron plates. The final grading as to color and clarity was done in New York after cutting and polishing. The sorting process at the mine was intended to remove undesirable material to facilitate easier and less costly handling and shipping.

The quality of color and hardness of turquoise from the Elizabeth Pocket contributed to southwest turquoise replacing Persian turquoise in the U.S. market. It was considered, with Courtland, Arizona and Cerrillos, as the best in the world and brought up to $20 per carat wholesale. Total sales from the Elizabeth Pocket are estimated between $2MM and $5MM of high-grade turquoise sold between 1891 and 1914.

The Azure Mining Company owed its success to a number of factors. First, the company principals were well capitalized and had extensive experience in the jewelry manufacturing and marketing business. Their agent in the field, Gyulo Armeny, was successful in accumulating a valuable group of claims. Perhaps most important was the skilled team the group hired to manage the mining operations. Felix Vogel was superintendent from the company's founding until 1901 and was responsible for the location of the Elizabeth Pocket that made the company's turquoise fortune. E.J. Franz succeeded him from 1901–1903. Thomas English was superintendent in 1904 when some fine bodies of turquoise were opened and the cut extended into the mountain another 75 feet.[25] E.R. Zalinski assumed the management of the mine for the year 1905 and was succeeded by W.R. Wade, who remained on the job until the company ceased significant turquoise mining during the next couple years.

Azure Turquoise Mine. Loading. Public domain.

Azure Turquoise Mine, Digging. Public domain.

"Azure Turquoises Do Not Change Color"

When Gyulo Armeny selected partners for his venture, he chose men that were not only well capitalized and able to provide financial stability for the fledging mine, but also were well-respected leaders in the New York jewelry market that knew how to fabricate jewelry and, even more importantly, how to sell it. Meyer Rothschild's brother Alonzo was publisher and co-owner of *The Jewelers' Circular-Weekly,* and these advertisements from *McClure's* and *Cosmopolitan* demonstrate the marketing edge the Azure Company had in branding their product for the retail trade.

Though it is true the Tiffany organization's total sales exceeded the others competing in the turquoise trade, their product line was also much larger. The *Blue Book* offered a full range of dry goods and household items as well as silverware and jewelry. William Alling, who was president of the ATC following its reorganization in 1897, was considered one of the largest jewelry manufacturers in New York. During the 1904 Paris World exposition, the Azure Mining Company had sales of $20,000 selling only turquoise jewelry, whereas Tiffany entered into almost every retail category and had sales of $1.5MM.

The smaller companies needed a marketing edge against such competition. The Azure Mining Company sought to exploit the hardness of the turquoise coming from the Elizabeth Pocket. Turquoise is a relatively soft mineral with a hardness ranging from 5 to 6 on the Mohs Hardness Scale. The softer the stone, the more readily it absorbed oils and changed color, usually blue to green. Considering the desired color at the time was the non-matrix, sky blue, we might imagine customers were not happy when this happened.

Azure was able to guarantee that their turquoise would not change color. The following advertisement from *The Jewelers' Circular* of September 7, 1898 stated:

> The limited supply and great demand for fine turquoise would have placed these gems among the most costly of the precious stones were it not for the fact that turquoises have rarely retained their beautiful color.
>
> An experience of seven years has demonstrated that among the products of various turquoise mines, Persian, Egyptian, and American, the stones of the Azure Mine have been unique.
>
> None of the "Azure" stones has changed color, and it is safe for a jeweler to sell a turquoise from the Azure Mining Company as it would be to sell a ruby or an emerald.
>
> To protect the trade against fraud and to emphasize our "guarantee" we mark every "Azure" turquoise by engraving a ring or circle on the back of the stone. None is genuine without this ring, which is the trademark registered in the United States and Europe.

The company registered the trademark in February 1894 with the Commissioner of Patents[26] and was included that year in the following advertisement from *Cosmopolitan* and became the basis of their marketing campaign. By 1898, that had developed to include a notarized guarantee from Mr. Meyer D. Rothschild himself. This showed the confidence the company had in the turquoise they were finding, because the Elizabeth Pocket had just begun producing turquoise and not enough time had passed for color fading to occur. Certainly the company principles felt they needed to counter the well-known brand of the competition with a little name-dropping of their own. Their efforts were successful; total sales from the Azure mine are estimated to have been more than double that of the ATC Tiffany mine, the second largest producer of the period.

"Azure Turquoise Guaranteed" advertisement.

Vick's Floral Guide 1894.

READY JAN. 1st.

Contains colored plates and illustrations of many novelties and specialties, among which are

Roses,
Chrysanthemums,
Vicks' New White Branching Aster,
Double Anemone Whirlwind, and
Maggie Murphy Potato.

Full descriptions of *Flowers, Vegetables, Mushrooms, Potatoes, Bulbs, &c.,* and how to plant them.

Send 10 cents for Floral Guide now and take time to make out order, the 10 cents may be deducted from first order.

JAMES VICK'S SONS, Rochester, N.Y.

52
Flowering Bulbs
$1.

Delivered anywhere, charges prepaid, planting instructions included, consisting of

3 Sweet Scented Jonquils,
10 large Golden Crocuses,
5 Snow Drops,
10 Blue Crocuses,
5 Hyacinths,
5 Double Tulips,   } In different colors.
5 Single Tulips,
5 Single Tulips—Yellow,
4 Daffodils.

These are the most desirable Bulbs for out door or window culture. You plant them now and they bloom in the Spring. Sure to bloom abundantly. Send for them at once, together with our catalogue of Hardy Trees, Shrubs, Roses, and Fruit.

Andorra Nurseries,
Chestnut Hill,   Philadelphia, Pa.
William Warner Harper, Manager.

About Turquoises

If cold December gave you birth,
The month of snow and ice and mirth,
Place on your hand a Turquoise blue,
Success will bless whate'er you do.

"**A Praiseworthy Departure.**—A New York company controlling the output of an American turquoise mine has inaugurated a departure as praiseworthy as it is unique. Turquoise has always been regarded as a capricious mineral, the color of which has been looked upon as no more stable than the affections of a coquette. . . . . . The company has determined to provide a means for identification. Its confidence in the merits of its product is necessarily attested by the trade-mark placed upon each turquoise from its mine. It says to the world: 'Here is a mark that all may see and know—a guaranty upon which our honor, our reputation, and our wealth are staked.'"—*Editorial Jewelers' Weekly, May 31, 1893.*

The product of the Azure Mining Company, which is sold and guaranteed by all first-class Jewelers, does not change color. Every

Azure Turquoise

is marked on the back with a circle or ring which is a registered trade-mark.

BE SURE THAT THE TURQUOISE YOU BUY HAS THIS MARK ON THE BACK.

STATE OF NEW YORK, } ss.
CITY AND COUNTY OF NEW YORK, }

M. D. Rothschild, being duly sworn, deposes and says that he is Secretary and Treasurer of the Azure Mining Company, a corporation duly organized under the laws of the State of New York, and doing business in New York City, and that he has had entire supervision of all the turquoises mined, cut and sold by said Azure Mining Co. for over two years past, and during that time not a single one of the "Azure" turquoises—either those sold or those retained in stock—has changed color in any respect.   M. D. ROTHSCHILD.

Sworn to and subscribed before me this 16th day of October, 1893, A.D.   JOHN H. RYAN,
Notary Public, New York County.

When you write, please mention "The Cosmopolitan."

Azure Guarantee from Meyer Rothschild advertisement.

In "The Azure Mine" advertisement.

At this time, it was a standard practice to identify jewelry brands with trademark images. Although it appears the Azure Mining Company was the first of the competing turquoise companies to do so, others followed quickly. In 1904, Fayette Jones reported that as a general practice the trademark was on the back of the gems: A for ATC, X for the Gem Turquoise and Copper Company, T for the Toltec Company, an ← for the Himalaya Company, as well as the O of the Azure. Although consumers expected to see the marks of the respective companies on the back of the turquoise they purchased, apparently only the Azure Company extended the guarantee that the stone would not change color, which must have been an advantage in the marketplace. Little, if any, of the turquoise pieces survived because they were used extensively in jewelry and unset stones were not often sold. Old turquoise pieces from the period must still exist, with the respective trademark concealed in the setting, although the authors have been unable to locate any known examples.

The Tiffany Brand

Throughout The Great American Turquoise Rush and continuing to today, people believed Tiffany and Co., including Charles L. Tiffany himself, owned and operated turquoise mines throughout the Southwest. In fact, as we have seen, although Tiffany and Co. was probably the period's largest single buyer of turquoise—purchasing from multiple sources—Charles Tiffany was invested only in the ATC as a bondholder and a stockholder. Neither he nor Tiffany and Co. ever operated any turquoise mining operations. Yet the allure of the Tiffany brand was strong, and many found it to their advantage to associate their efforts with such a well-known name.

The proliferation of the Tiffany myth began during the boom. William E. Hidden, who partnered with Armeny and Tannenbaum in the emerald mine in North Carolina, was also interested in turquoise. During a trip in March of 1892, he traveled through the Burro area and Hachita before finally seeking turquoise in the Jarilla Mountains. In an article from November 1893 in *The Jewelers' Circular,* he commented that the Azure Mining Company had shipped 50 kilograms of high-grade turquoise during the prior 12 months.[27] Yet we find in a January 27, 1893 article in the *Silver City Enterprise* a very different version of the story:

William E. Hidden of Newark, the mineralogist, has been engaged in successful mining operations in New Mexico during the last few months.

Mr. Hidden's trip to New Mexico was for the specific purpose of developing turquoise mines in the Burro Mountains, and he was backed by the company in which Tiffany, the jeweler, is financially interested. The capital stock was $1,000,000 and on this a six percent dividend has been declared from the earnings of nine months' work at the mines. The work of Mr. Hidden and his assistants is said to have resulted in the discovery of turquoise equal to the best found in Persia. The new company is now the leading producer of turquoise in the world, as the output is larger than that of the Persian mines. Most of the stockholders live in New York and Charles L. Tiffany is said to be among the heaviest.[28]

Although it may have been true at the time that the Muñiz Tiffany mine at Cerrillos was the largest turquoise producer, it was soon overtaken by the Azure mine when the Elizabeth Pocket came on line in 1893. The ATC had no claims in the Burros, and no evidence exists that Charles L. Tiffany ever invested with any of the leading companies that mined turquoise in the district over the next decade.

The Porterfield Brothers

The turquoise companies vying for dominance during The Great American Turquoise Rush often followed the same pattern. Local miners and prospectors located and filed the claims. Entrepreneurs, primarily from the New York jewelry market, organized and financed the company, with the East coast partners overseeing cutting and processing the rough stone and a supervisor overseeing the turquoise mining. Often the east coast investors had little contact with the local community where the turquoise was mined. The Porterfields were the exception to that rule.

Melvin W. Porterfield was born in 1855 and his brother William C. in 1858, both in Fairfield, Illinois in the southern part of the state. M.W. graduated from National Normal University in Lebanon, Ohio in 1877, and by 1880 he and his brother were owners of the Porterfield Brothers drug store in Fairfield. In 1887, W.C. moved to Silver City, New Mexico Territory and M.W. joined him in 1888, when they established the Porterfield Drug Company. They owned and operated the store until 1909, when it was sold and became the Howell Drug Company.

Melvin W. Porterfield, Courtesy of Palace of the Governors Photo Archives (NMHM/DCA) negative number 50571.

The brothers wasted no time becoming involved in the community. In 1889 W.C. assisted in drafting a pharmacy law for the territory and served for 16 years on the Board of Pharmacy. He was active in the New Mexico National Guard, rising to the rank of colonel and participating in the Mexico Punitive Expedition against Pancho Villa under General Pershing, and on staff duty with the U.S. Army during World War I. He was active in the Masonic Order and in territorial Republican politics, serving as a representative for New Mexico at President Taft's inauguration. M.W. was a probate judge from 1890–1892, and later served on the board of county commissioners, but he is best remembered for his interest in local mining, specifically turquoise. Imagine Melvin out with his prospector buddies searching leads on the ancient turquoise diggings and successfully locating and filing claims on a series of properties, as his younger brother William was diligently minding the store to provide some financial stability to an effort known for its hit–or–miss cash flow.

In an age of big box stores and strip malls, it is difficult to imagine life in a frontier town in the territory of New Mexico in 1888. The area was just beginning to establish rules of law and order, following a period of near lawlessness during the previous decade. A town's society was built around the foundations of government, a county sheriff (also responsible for tax assessment and collection), a town Marshall and judge responsible for law enforcement, and a post office. Equally important were the centers for commerce and communication: the train depot, general store, barbershop, and drug store. For miners used to spending long periods in the mountains, a trip to town certainly meant a visit to the drug store and, along with the other retail establishments, served as a conduit for information and socializing, including a good dose of gossip.

Any community prides itself on the success of its local people. Society during the late Victorian age was perhaps even more parochial and closely tied to relationships of family, religion, and politics than ours today. It is understandable that model businessmen and pillars of the community like the Porterfields were seen as perfect representatives for the turquoise industry, certainly a contrast to the outsiders represented by the Azure Turquoise Company, which was the most successful of all the companies operating in the Burros and in the entire Territory.

In the *History of New Mexico Volume 2,* the claim was made that M.W. Porterfield "may be considered the father of turquoise mining on a commercial scale in New Mexico, if not in the United States".[29] Although the statement may be a bit of a superlative judgment, there is no doubt that Porterfield played a significant role in the development of turquoise mining in the Burros, beginning with his involvement in securing the claims for the Azure Mining Company. It's possible to speculate that although this initial foray into mining in establishing locations and claims was financially rewarding, Porterfield must have rankled at the lost opportunity when Armeny and the New York investors struck a turquoise bonanza in the Elizabeth Pocket, and he was determined to mount a successful competitive challenge to their dominance.

He used his economic and political prominence to secure an important position at the 1893 Columbian Exposition in Chicago with the mines and mineral exhibit that would have increased his standing in the world of both mineralogists and jewelers. At the 1904 Louisiana Purchase Exposition in St. Louis, he managed the New Mexico exhibit, which had as its centerpiece a replica of a Porterfield turquoise mine. This exhibit represented the centerpiece of an extensive New Mexico contingent, including exhibitions in the respective buildings for education, forestry, horticulture, agriculture, manufacture, and mining. The territory's commitment to the importance of this exhibit was evident in the $30,000 the legislature spent. An article in the *Silver City Enterprise* from August 7, 1903 quotes the wording from the mining exhibit application.

We wish to construct as near as possible a facsimile of a turquoise mine and to ship a sufficient quantity of the rock, from a mine, to line the walls so that some of the rock will show the turquoise embedded in the matrix exactly as it occurs in the geological formation. We purpose to show the methods employed in operating the mines and extracting stone from the matrix and to have lapidist cutting, polishing and finishing the gem ready for commerce thus showing the entire process.

Although he parlayed this prominence into being considered the Turquoise King, his actual success in putting together a competitive operation to mine, process, and sell turquoise was never as successful as the more prominent leaders in New Mexico, the Azure Mining Company, and the ATC.

M.W. Porterfield, with his former mining partner Nick Rascom, was largely responsible for the success of Gyulo Armeny in accumulating the claims that were successful for the Azure Mining Company. Although Porterfield had received a significant payment of $14,000 for his claims, by 1893 and the discovery of the Elizabeth Pocket it must have been clear he was on the short end of that deal. For all of their prominence in the community, the Porterfield's remain a bit of a turquoise enigma. Their names always seem to appear relative to the acquisition of claims into a series of turquoise companies beginning with the Azure Mining Company, but once they were paid for the claims they had no further involvement.

Following the sale of claims to Gyulo Armeny in 1891, M.W. Porterfield attended the Colombian Exposition in Chicago and was involved with the mining exhibit. We have seen in his letter to L. Bradford Prince of the New Mexico Turquoise Company that he proposed a merger of half his interest in a turquoise property in the Burros with similar sale for the Persian held by Prince. The newly created company would own half interests in the two properties, with Porterfield retaining half interest in the Burro property, and Prince's group half interest in the Persian. Each would have been paid well for their interests. Although we do not know the name of the property, we may assume Porterfield acted as agent for other interests. In December of 1894, he was listed as owner of the Castilian claim in Cow Springs, which today is known as White Signal, and we know that in 1897 both brothers were active in the succession of deals that resulted in the Calaite claims, the site of the Indian turquoise diggings, being transferred to T.S. Parker. In the 1893 Mining Records of the U.S. report, Kunz wrote that Porterfield had found traces of turquoise one half mile from the Azure mine and had made excavations of about 18 feet showing turquoise of the characteristic green color often found in the Burros.[30]

By 1902 there were five claims associated with the Porterfield mines, as referenced in an article from the *Silver City Independent* of February 18, 1902, stating the Porterfield brothers had a small number of workers on five claims and were taking out and shipping some good turquoise. By 1906, we find claims on the following mines: Turquoise Gem, Silver City Gem, Azure Gem, Zuni, and later the Azure Gem Extension. We know the brothers were selling turquoise locally from a Christmas Day 1903 advertisement in the *Silver City Enterprise:*

Turquoise

Every patriotic citizen of New Mexico should wear a Turquoise, since this territory supplies the world with this gem. We have Turquoise Jewelry, Turquoise Rings. Turquoise Brooches Turquoise Lace Pins, Matrix Stones Unset, Shirt Studs, Sleeve Buttons, Gem Stones Unset. Our Souvenir Turquoise Pins made of the unpolished stone showing a specimen of this gem stone as it comes from the mines, make a nice present. At Porterfield's.[31]

Porterfield turquoise mine, looking south. The camp is on the left. D.B. Sterrett, *U.S. Geological Survey*, 42.

Porterfield turquoise mine looking northeast.
D.B. Sterrett, *U.S. Geological Survey*, 43.

We know these products were for sale at the St. Louis Louisiana Purchase Exposition in 1904 because concession revenue of $308.35 gross and $77.34 net was reported for the Porterfield brothers, and $528.90 gross and $141.70 net for Porterfield. Company.[32] It appears that the Porterfields had larger distribution as well. Mrs. W.C. Totty said in 1937 that they had a contract from Albert Larson and Co., whose firm was competing on Maiden Lane in New York with the Rothschilds (which must be presumed to reference the Azure Mining Company). Certainly the Porterfield brothers were a major player in turquoise in the Burros and by all appearances were positioning themselves to challenge the predominance of the Azure Mining Company.

On January 16, 1906 the Porterfield Turquoise Mines Co. was incorporated in the Territory of Oklahoma. In spite of the name the purpose of the company was "to discover, locate, buy, own, sell, lease, develop, and operate gold, silver, quicksilver, copper, manganese and other mines, quartz, gravel, cement, coal, mineral, or oil deposits, mining claims, minerals and precious stones of every kind and description". In addition the company would be wholesale and retail jewelers, build and operate tramways, sailing vessels or barges, as well as operating boarding houses and hotels. Nowhere in this long list does the word turquoise appear except in the name of the corporation. Even more curious neither Porterfield brother is listed on the board of directors who consist of A.P. Hale and E. Buckley from San Francisco, California and C.V. Pattison from Guthrie, Oklahoma. The company was capitalized at $2MM but with an odd choice of share valuation. One million two hundred thousand shares were given a par value of $1 each and an additional eight thousand shares a par value of $100 each.

The lack of involvement of the brothers in a company bearing their name, especially after the central role they had played in promoting turquoise on behalf of the Territory and in their own business, requires some speculation. It may be that the brothers felt they could not compete with the other competitors in the turquoise market, so they raised capital from outside investors, Hale, Buckley, and Pattison. Perhaps the second group of stock valued at the higher par value was used to buy out the turquoise claims and other mineral interests the brothers had. The boarding house project appears to have been one of the first projects of the new corporation. This may be seen in the following report from the *Silver City Enterprise:*

> Will Build Cottages. The Porterfield Turquoise Co., which holds upwards of 200 acres between Tyrone and Leopold in the Burro Mtns. Is preparing to build a series of cottages along the main traveled road between the two camps for the use of American workman and their families."[33]

This effort anticipated the development of the Phelps Dodge model workers' community in Tyrone, created by Mabel Dodge, designed by Bertram Goodhue at a cost of over $1MM and completed in 1915 when the area was being mined for copper. Prospects looked good for the Porterfield Turquoise Company as Sterrett, who had succeeded Kunz as editor, described in the 1906 *MRUS.* He reported they had extended the number and depth of the shafts, with turquoise occurring along a belt about 300 feet wide and 600 feet long and producing a large quantity of good quality turquoise.[34]

Unfortunately the timing of the ambitious expansion of the Porterfield Turquoise Mines Co. enterprise corresponded with a drop in the market, partly due to declining interest in turquoise jewelry but certainly made worse by the financial collapse of 1907 and the recession that followed. John Cowen reported in 1911: "Many believe that if the turquoise market had not faltered soon after the turn of the twentieth century, the Porterfield mines possibly could have rivaled even those of the ATC at Cerrillos in both quantity and quality."[35] Regardless, M.W. Porterfield will be remembered as a community leader, successful in several business activities, and perhaps the most active and effective spokesperson for turquoise during The Great American Turquoise Rush.

The Parker Mines

The Great American Turquoise Rush encompasses the growth of business trusts built by the legendary John D. Rockefeller, Andrew Carnegie, Cornelius Vanderbilt, and financier J.P. Morgan. It was expected one dominant operator would control every phase of a business sector and turquoise mining was no different, from mining to processing and final distribution. The company that succeeded in gaining this position could control supply and, assuming a stable or growing demand for the product, the price. By the end of the century, two companies were dominant in the turquoise trade operating in New Mexico: The ATC in Cerrillos, with close ties to the distribution network including Tiffany and Co., but also with other involvement including William Alling and the Azure Mining Company, which counted among its investors and officers Jewish leaders in the jewelry and precious gems community that were becoming a strong presence in the New York market.

Although these two companies accounted for the majority of sales during the period of 1891–1899, financial difficulties weakened the ATC. The company was successful in mining and selling turquoise, but less adept at maintaining a viable financial position. By the end of the decade, the Azure Mining Company was the undisputed leader in the turquoise trade. Others were keen to usurp that position and become the new dominant player.

Thomas S. Parker's past was somewhat mysterious. He was born in Iowa in 1846 and served as a captain in the 70th Iowa Volunteer Calvary and was a telegraph operator before heading west in 1883. In an obituary from the *Silver City Enterprise* dated July 13, 1917, he had first arrived in the west from Iowa to work on the construction of the Atlantic and Pacific Railroad, which started west of Albuquerque. He found his way to Silver City and became a significant participant in the mining activities in the area. Yet another obituary from the *El Paso Herald* of July 16, 1917 makes the following claim:

News has been received here of the death in Rochester, Minn., of Capt.

Thomas S. Parker, retired pioneer mine owner of the Tyrone district, near Silver City, N. M., at the age of 70 years. About 40 years ago Capt. Parker, civil war veteran, plains railroad builder and Indian scout in the campaign under Gen. Crook against the Apaches, rode across the little pine clad valley where Tyrone, the mine and smelter city of the Phelps Dodge corporation, now is located, decided that he would settle there and did so later, acquiring an immense acreage of land covering copper and turquoise veins. He promoted a number of exploitation companies, made and lost several fortunes and finally sold the last of his holdings to the Phelps Dodge agents in 1914, breaking up his home in the little sanatorium city he had built and moving to El Paso.

Although Parker made his fortune in copper by selling the Burro Chief Copper Company, which he formed in 1909, to Phelps Dodge for $2MM, his goal was to establish a dominant turquoise company.

John Coleman and William Foley had filed their claim on the Calaite, on the site of the old Indian turquoise mine on November 15, 1890. Although they continued to file the annual Proof of Labor required to maintain their claim, nothing indicates they worked it for turquoise to any measurable degree. Ownership expanded when, in May of 1891, Foley and Coleman sold or transferred one-third interest to Florence E. Dorsey. In 1895, a flurry of Calaite interest transfers began, resulting in the Porterfield brothers and Thomas Parker and his business associates, John M. Wiley and James E. Harvey, holding the claim by early 1896.

At this point, a series of business transactions commenced that provided insight into the market for turquoise and the competition for dominance in the trade. The Occidental and Oriental Turquoise and Mining Company was incorporated under the laws of the Territory of New Mexico on March 29, 1897, with a four-member board of directors: Thomas S. Parker, John M. Wiley, James E. Harvey, and James J. Sheridan, all residents of Grant County. The company's stated purpose was:

> ...to mine turquoise and other precious metals, to locate, buy, sell, and hold mines and mining claims; to carry on a general mining business and milling business, and to have, hold, and transfer real estate and other property necessary and incident to the conduct of such business.

Yet even as the company was being formed, other negotiations were in play. This was at the height of The Great American Turquoise Rush, and hundreds of thousands of dollars' worth of turquoise was at stake. Competition for the business was intense both from established participants in the jewelry industry and from speculators who seemed intent on exploiting an opportunity. The Azure Mining Company was on solid financial footing due, we might speculate, to the business acumen of its managers and shareholders, whereas the ATC filed for bankruptcy in 1897 because the bank foreclosed on their loan.

The bank foreclosure occurred in spite of the principal of the $250,000 note having been reduced by over $150,000 since its inception in late 1891. After only six months in operation, the company paid a dividend to its stockholders, the amount of which is uncertain. The *Silver City Enterprise* reports it as 6 percent of the value of the total capitalization of $1MM or $60,000, a considerable sum at that time. The *New York Times* reports the dividend at 6 cents per share (10,000 at the time) or $600. Operating costs at the Tiffany Mine were about $6,000 per year, which would indicate the company had generated a minimum cash flow of $250,000 over the preceding four plus years. In any mining operation where supply is unpredictable, the probability of not being able to meet expenses is always high when owners remove capital as fast as it comes in.

Still, in the Burros, the Azure operation was a cash cow and the lure of moving into this market was very attractive, and prospective markets had extended across the ocean. In an article from a London journal, *Ladies Home,* quoted extensively in a *Silver City Enterprise* article the exotic history of turquoise from its Persian roots leading to the present:

> The oriental turquoise of Persia has been famed from time immemorial for its beautiful coloring. In recent years the supply from the Persian mines has gradually fallen off until the product from that source has almost entirely ceased. While the supply has diminished the beautiful stone has continued to grow in favor and has become fashionable so much that it has become impossible to supply the demand, especially for large stones of the best quality. In 1891 Mr. N.C. Rascom, a veteran miner, discovered the turquoise mines of the Azure Company. But little was known of the value of turquoise mines or the precious product until some of the great New York jewelers, learning of the find, sent an agent to investigate its merit, and being satisfied of its great value purchased the Santa Fe claim. The Azure mining company was organized and systematic development

inaugurated. In a short time this mine became the principal producer of turquoise in the world. It is claimed that the mine has produced three million dollars of turquoise in the past four years.[36]

This article certainly appeared to be a public relations effort, because it was sent to a publication with specific information for inclusion. It is unlikely the editors and writers of a ladies fashion journal in London knew the detailed operations of a turquoise mine in New Mexico. This was even more evident when the writer went into the following detail regarding the value of the turquoise mined:

> And this estimate (three million) appears reasonable when it is considered that an ounce, troy weight equals one hundred and fifty carats, computing on the basis of the American carat 3.2 grains (the English and French carats are lighter, being 3.1 and 3.18 grains respectively) and that is for the year 1894 alone. 300 pounds weight *avoirdupois,* or 656,250 carats of assorted turquoise was shipped from the mine. Allowing that only 20 per cent of the product or 131,250 carats would sell as first class stones at $6.00 per carat, the proceeds would be $787,500 yearly, to which is to be added the value of the second class material which is utilized in mosaic work and inlaying.[37]

Although the upper-class Victorian readers might have been a bit puzzled by the financial details, another indication of the article's purpose was in the following quote: "The turquoise obtained from the mines of the Azure Company and from the Calaite group adjoining excels all other gems of the species, even those of the celebrated Persian mines at Abu Riah and Nishapur." The article ends with a return to the sort of flowery prose Victorian ladies preferred:

> The New Mexico mines start from a pit dug by the Aztecs centuries ago, two round Aztec hammers having been found there quite recently, which can now be seen in London, thereby proving that the subjects of Montezuma were as keenly alive to the witchery of the stone as the ladies of London and New York. The district of Silver City is no doubt a rich gem field where Nature is holding treasured up stores of all grades of turquoise which can be easily won to increase the pleasure of the world.[38]

This reference to a group of claims that had produced no turquoise at the time of this publication is readily explained, albeit cloaked in mystery. The *Silver City Enterprise* article adds to the extended quote from *Ladies Home* with the information that:

> The Turquoise Syndicate of London of which Mr. Harry S. Foster, M.P. is chairman has now assumed control of the Calaite group, and a force of miners were put to work during the past week and the Calaite will soon be a strong competitor for first place with its great sister, the Azure.

Sir Harry Seymour Foster was indeed a conservative Member of Parliament from Portsmouth who founded a successful chartered accountants firm, Foster, Hight and Company, and was the managing director of the London and Colonial Finance Corporation. His distinguished political career included London alderman, Suffolk M.P., and council general of Persia from 1894–1903. In 1918, he was knighted for his many years of public service. It is unlikely he was the Harry S. Foster promoting the North American Turquoise Syndicate, who Spence referenced as having promoted 60 companies of Anglo-American mining concerns.[39] Perhaps he was the Harry Seymour Foster referenced in connection with the case of Stewart and others versus Foster for the recovery of £1,500 for illegally collecting commissions acting as agent for the plaintiffs in the purchase of estates in Ceylon. It is challenging to understand how a successful chartered accountant running a business, serving as London alderman, M.P., and council-general to Persia, would have either the time or inclination to deal in the promotion of questionable speculative stock ventures.

Although we may never be certain of the identity and background of Harry S. Foster, we can be certain that English companies had been investing in U.S. mining operations since the 1860s. To the investors of late Victorian Great Britain, the richest empire on the planet, the United States must have represented what later investors considered an emerging market offering the opportunity for high returns for those willing to undertake substantial risks. Mining ventures were often promoted in respected London journals such as *The Strand* or *The Times,* thus it was not surprising to see the North American Turquoise Syndicate promoting its venture in a journal, although one more suited to fashion than finance.

More evidence that both this article and the one in the *Ladies Home* were part of a coordinated public relations and marketing campaign by Parker and

Foster was the fact that the entire section of the October 1898 article from the *Silver City Enterprise* detailing the specific production amounts and value of turquoise being mined was taken verbatim from an April 14, 1897 article in the same paper titled, "TURQUOISE MINING, The Most Profitable Branch of the Mining Industry." The article stated: "The Occidental and Oriental Turquoise Mining Company was organized about a month ago for the purpose of working mines adjacent to the Azure Companies' claims."[40] Mr. H.E. Oppenheimer, a prominent New York City diamond dealer, was listed as the company president, a connection that proved important in the future developments of the Parker mines.

Throughout 1897, Parker had been in the process of securing claims for his turquoise company, possibly with the intention of flipping those properties should the opportunity be available. Records show an escrow was subscribed when Parker agreed to sell the block of half interest in the Calaite and full interest in Calaite no. 2, Baby Blue, California no. 2, Leap Year, Monmouth, Peerless, and Bonanza to Henry Wilson of St. Louis for the sum of £60,000, if the deal was completed by June 25, 1897.[41] At the same time, M.W. Porterfield agreed to sell his half interest in the Calaite for $12,500, if Parker completed the transaction by July 1, 1897. The first transaction was denominated in pounds Sterling, which indicates Mr. Wilson represented a group of British investors. The deal did not go through. Parker persevered and on February 5, 1898, W.C. Porterfield and his wife Maggie, who had received the interest from his brother following the botched sale to Parker on July 1, 1897, sold their half interest in the Calaite to the Occidental and Oriental Turquoise Mining Company (OandOTMC) for the same price as previously offered, $12,500. This gave Parker and the OandOTMC complete control over the claims, which became known as the Parker mines.

Evidently Parker continued his quest to secure foreign investors. On April 5, 1898, the OandOTMC deeded to the North American Turquoise Syndicate these claims for the price of £24,000, less than half of what had been structured in the previous year's failed deal. The amount became a moot point because, however adept Foster may have been at promoting the venture, he was unable to come up with the money. Three months later on July 7, 1898, the OandOTMC deeded the claims to Thomas S. Parker. Parker may have been disappointed at the failure of these business deals, but he was no doubt grateful later as these claims not only were profitable for mining turquoise, but also, more importantly, formed the core of his future copper interests.

Parker had control of his mines, but was short of working capital to develop them. Although he had local partners in the OandOTMC who shared his mining knowledge, he lacked working capital and the ability to process and market the finished stones. On July 16, 1901, the *Silver City Independent* announced under the heading "News of the Mines, Mills, and Miners," that the Gem Turquoise and Copper Company of West Virginia, GTandCC, had filed articles of incorporation with the territorial secretary. The company listed capital of $250,000 divided into 250,000 shares. The directors of the company were listed as: Augustus K. Sloan, Frank T. Sloan, and John W. Block of Brooklyn, New York; Frederick J. Essig, Chicago; Frank Squire, Alfred Krower, and Henry E. Oppenheimer, New York; Thomas S. Parker, Silver City; and Lucius P. Deming, New Haven, Connecticut. Each of these directors had subscribed to $5,000 of common stock, with $500 paid up. John Block was the brother of Wesley Block, who had purchased the Persian claim from Foley and who partnered with Lippman Tannenbaum in a claim in the Jarilla Mountains. The notice continued:

> The offices of the company are at 23 Maiden Lane, New York. It will conduct mining operations in Grant County, in the Burro mountain district. The new company has secured the turquoise and copper claims, commonly known as the Parker mines, consisting of nineteen in all, of which six are turquoise and thirteen copper. Thomas S. Parker, who is the general manager and superintendent of the company, left last night for New York City, and will return here and assume personal conduct of the operation just as soon as he can transact some important business matters in the east. In the meantime operations are being pushed forward at the mines by a force of ten men, under John M. Wiley. The same force has been at work for two months past, but the new company did not desire any publicity of their intentions until the corporation had been organized and other details perfected. The property acquired by the company is regarded by well-informed mining men as among the best in this southwestern country, especially the turquoise mines, which have been operated successfully for years past and have yielded a large and valuable output, the gems being of superior quality. It was from this property that the turquoise which was presented to Mrs. McKinley at the time of the presidential reception at Deming in May was taken. The company will cut and market their own turquoise, and for this purpose Henry E. Oppenheimer has been designated as European agent and

Albert Lorsh and Co., of New York City, agent for the United States and Canada. The president of the company is August K. Sloan, who is one of the best known jewelers in the United States, being president of the jeweler's board of trade of New York and holding a similar office with the jeweler's association of the same city. His son, Frank T. Sloan, is secretary of the company. A fifty-ton concentrating mill will be erected for the treatment of the copper ores. This operation means much for the Burro Mountains in particular and Grant County in general."[42]

Leveraging his contact with Oppenheimer, who had been listed as president of the OandOTMC, Parker had arranged for $45,000 in working capital, pledged with $4,500 paid for current expenses. At Cerrillos, the ATC had employed five men under Patrick McNulty to mine the Tiffany, and had monthly expenses of about $500. With a workforce of twice that, the GTandCC had cash on hand for about four months of expenses, with sufficient capital pledged to ensure operations for the foreseeable future, regardless of sales from turquoise production. Parker had also assembled a team that, in addition to having capital resources for investment, brought a wealth of experience in processing, fabricating, and selling jewelry. The GTandCC address was 23 Maiden Lane, almost adjacent to the offices of the Azure Mining Company at 10 Maiden Lane, and no doubt the message was not lost on the Kahn brothers and Meyer Rothschild.

Frederick Essig, who was mentioned in M.W. Porterfield's failed attempt to partner with Prince and merge with the New Mexico Turquoise Company in 1893, had finally succeeded in aligning himself with a company that could provide a ready source of turquoise for his lapidary business. The Sloans were leaders in the New York jewelry trade and knew how to fabricate or source jewelry production. Respected agents were also in to distribute the product in the United States, Canada, and Europe. Parker was responsible for onsite production and management, with John Wiley as mine manager.

This effort must have been especially rewarding to August K. Sloan, who had been part of the failed attempt to build a similar organization to challenge the Azure Mining Company in 1899 while he was serving as secretary of the North American Turquoise Syndicate. In Chapter 2, we learned this effort was the brainchild of A. McGregor Leffingwell, who was long on ambition but short on implementation. It was Leffingwell who attempted to option the properties of the ATC in Cerrillos and boldly approached *The Jewelers' Circular*, openly boasting at how "his idea was to do with turquoise what had been done with diamonds by the DeBeers Consolidated Mines Co of South Africa." The article continued:

He was hopeful of getting all the mines into the concern, and in any case believed his company would be large enough to force a general co-operation in regard to prices and methods, even if there be no consolidation of interests. He exhibited a map of the mines already acquired and from it is to be seen that they quite surround the Azure and American mines.[43]

We know Leffingwell had accomplished nothing of the sort. The ATC controlled their Cerrillos claims, with minor competition from the New Mexico Turquoise Company and a few other smaller mining operations, and Parker, through the OandTMC, controlled the Calaite group of claims southeast of those of the Azure. Sloan likely was relieved when he found Thomas Parker, a man who could match his aspirations with the necessary practical reality of accumulating a group of claims. It had been reported as early as 1896 that Parker was making shipments of turquoise to Tiffany jewelers of New York.[44] Although it appeared he was regularly mining claims in the area with varying degrees of success, the consolidation of the OandOTMC into the GTandCC established an organization that was positioned to challenge the Azure Mining Company and the ATC as the leader in turquoise production.

Some questions remain regarding the company's formation. The authors could find no record of the existence of a corporation of this name in either the records of the secretary of state of West Virginia or the territorial records. The records could have been lost, filed in another jurisdiction, or never existed. This group of established, experienced businesspeople would not have any incentive to misrepresent the existence of a corporation. Records show that Parker retained ownership of the claims he received from the OandOTMC and these became the basis for the Burro Chief Copper Company that he incorporated in 1905 and later sold to Phelps Dodge for $2MM.

Turquoise production in the Burros, robust in 1901, diminished after 1909. The owners of the Gem Turquoise and Copper Company evidently saw the proverbial writing on the wall. Although they were set up to exploit the available opportunity at the time, as seasoned trade professionals they understood the whims and impact of unpredictable fashion trends. This prescience is evident in the name of the company and in the formation of an onsite copper-ore-concentrating mill. This forethought enriched Thomas S. Parker—railway worker, cavalry captain and Indian scout, and turquoise miner—who became wealthy from the sale of copper-bearing real estate. This also turned out to be the direction the Azure Mining Company followed when the directors sold out to Phelps Dodge many years later.

Burro Mountain turquoise (Tyrone). Private collection. Photo courtesy Michael Gomez and Teena Lee Ryan.

Notes

1. *Silver City Enterprise,* October 5, 1906.
2. C.L. Knaus, "Sky Stones," *New Mexico Magazine,* March, 1948, 23.
3. C.H. Snow, "Turquois in Southwestern New Mexico," *American Journal of Science,* vol. 41, 1891, 511.
4. *Grant County Mining Records Book 15,* 54.
5. C.H. Snow, "Turquois in Southwestern New Mexico," *American Journal of Science,* vol. 41, 1891, 511.
6. *Grant County Mining Records Book 15,* 55.
7. *Grant County Mining Deeds Book 27,* 327–328.
8. *Grant County Mining Deeds Book 14,* 681–682.
9. *Grant County Mining Deeds Book 27,* 533–534.
10. *Grant County Mining Records Book 14,* 338–339.
11. *Grant County Mining Records Book 31,* 73–74.
12. *Grant County Mining Records Book 27,* 362–363.
13. *Grant County Mining Records Book 14,* 363–364.
14. M.I. Jacobson, "Lippman Tannenbaum: President of the Himalaya Mining Company and a Difficult Person," *Mineral News,* September 2010, 6.
15. Ibid.
16. Ibid.
17. *Silver City Enterprise,* July 1, 1892.
18. *Silver City Enterprise,* September 9, 1892.
19. *Mineral Resources of the United States, 1892,* (1893) 764.
20. D.B. Sterrett, *Mineral Resources of the United States, 1907,* 830.
21. Ibid., 829.
22. E.R. Zalinski, "Turquoise Mining in the Burro Mountains, New Mexico," *Economic Geology* vol.2, No 5, July-August 1907, 476.
23. A.E. Rogge and Kristopher S. Shepard, *Supplemental Evaluation of Archaeological Sites Recorded by Surveys for the Proposed Little Rock Mine in Grant County, New Mexico,* 1996.
24. Zalinski, 1907, 475–476.
25. *Silver City Enterprise,* December 23, 1904.
26. Commissioner of Patents, *Annual Report for the Year 1894* (1895), 698.
27. W.E. Hidden, "New Mines of Turquoise in New Mexico," *The Jewelers' Circular,* Nov. 1, 1893.
28. *Silver City Enterprise,* January 27, 1893, and Higbie, 1971.
29. G.B. Anderson, *History of New Mexico, Its Resources and People,* vol. ii, Los Angeles: Pacific States Publishing: 1907).
30. Kunz, *Mineral Resources of the United States, 1893.*
31. *Silver City Enterprise,* December 25, 1903, 4.
32. D.R. Francis, *The Universal Exposition of 1904,* vol.1.
33. *Silver City Enterprise,* September 28, 1906.
34. Sterrett, *Mineral Resources of the United States,* 1906, 831.
35. J. L. Cowen, *Turquoise Mines of New Mexico,* Mineral Collector, vol.15, pp.110-112. 1908..
36. *Silver City Enterprise,* October 10, 1898, quoting from August 6, 1898 *Ladies Home.*
37. Ibid.
38. Ibid.
39. C.C. Spence, *British Investments and the American Mining Frontier, 1860-1901,* New York, Taylor and Francis, 2000), 40.

40. *Grant County Mining Deeds Book 33,* 594.
41. *Silver City Enterprise,* April 14, 1897, 3.
42. *Silver City Independent,* July 16, 1901.
43. *The Jewelers' Circular,* October 18, 1899.
44. *Silver City Enterprise,* December 22, 1896.

4

Hachita and Jarilla

Hachita

achita and Jarilla represent locations of great promise and great disappointment in the story of The Great American Turquoise Rush. As the turquoise boom began to gather steam in 1891 and 1892, it spawned intense competition among groups who sought to establish operations over a broad area. The intent of these companies was to control as much of the production and supply as possible in order to influence price.

The Little Hatchet Mountains are located about 7 miles southwest of the town of Hachita and about 80 miles south of Silver City in the most southern part of Grant County. There are two towns named Hachita; Old Hachita and New Hachita with the mines located primarily at Old Hachita. Hachita is the Spanish word for "little hatchet." The area was sparsely populated during the Spanish occupation because the Apaches claimed this land, and their response to any who did not respect that consideration was fierce. The Spanish had reported old turquoise diggings in the area. In the early 1870s, in spite of frequent furnace-like heat and the lack of water, prospectors began working the area for lead, copper, silver, and turquoise. In 1877, the Eureka Mining District was established.

As was the case in Cerrillos and in the Burro Mountains, prospectors following reports of prehistoric turquoise mines made the first claims in the Little Hatchet Mountains, which we will refer to as Hachita. The initial development of the turquoise deposits in the Eureka District of Grant County occurred in the latter 1880s, when Con Ryan and Sterling Burwell reopened some ancient workings they believed to be precious Aztec or Spanish metal mines.[1] Ryan filed a number of claims in 1890,[2] but probably soon allowed those to lapse in the absence of a market for turquoise and no economic incentive to provide the $100 per claim annual proof of labor assessment filing, which would have been a considerable investment at that time.

During a trip in March 1892, W.E. Hidden related that to access Hachita "one must take a dreary ride of 22 miles over the most desolate prairie country." He worked in the area for several weeks to open some of the prehistoric diggings, but concluded, "The isolation of the place, the scarcity of water, and the rarity of fine turquoise prompted me to cease work there altogether."[3]

In spite of Hidden's lack of enthusiasm for the area, interest in the turquoise deposits began to grow. Archie Young and F.A. Thetge had located the Montezuma, Idaho, King Solomon, Turquoise no.1, Turquoise no. 2, and Aztec claims. On July 13, 1891, they attempted to sell one-third interest in those mines to J.F. Price of El Paso Texas for $1,500.[4] That deal never was completed because Young and Thetge, each with half interest, relocated the group without Price in October 1892.[5]

About this time, Herbert A. Thomas, originally from Cook County, Illinois, and Harry Wood, from Springfield, Missouri, located three claims in the district. The first was the Woodbert, located on September 14, 1892 about a mile west of the Hornet mine.[6] They relocated this claim the following year to demonstrate they had performed the required annual assessment work. On October 14, 1892, they located the Herbert claim about a mile northwest of Turquoise Mountain or, to be more precise, three quarters of a mile northwest of Sterling Burwell's residence and one quarter north of Dug Out Wagon Road near the Montezuma and Turquoise claims of Young and Thetge.[7] On April 26, 1893, a third claim, the Tiffany, was located northwest of the Montezuma claim.[8] The next day, Thomas and Wood purchased Young and Thetge's Montezuma and Aztec claims for a combined sum of $500, thus giving them a total of five claims.[9]

While they were in the process of acquiring these claims, they must have been acting as agents of the ATC of New York, which was operating the Muñiz mine (aka Tiffany) in Cerrillos. A clear indication of this was the name they chose for their claim, the Tiffany, made just days prior to the sale of their claims to the ATC. The ATC was intent on diversifying and increasing their hold on the turquoise market, and on May 2, 1893, the company purchased Thomas and Wood's complete holdings of five claims for $20,000 and 7 percent of the gross proceeds from all the mines the company owned, the Woodbert, Herbert, Tiffany, Montezuma, and Aztec. This was an incredible deal for Thomas and Wood—although the Muñiz mine at Cerrillos yielded turquoise worth millions over the next few years, the mines at Hachita were never more than marginally developed and only the Herbert would ever produce any quantity of turquoise. Not only did Thomas and Wood make a great deal, but also they hedged their bets by purchasing the True Blue claim from John Anders on April 27, 1893, which they did not sell to the ATC.

Looking northeast along vein of the Herbert claim of the ATC.
D.B. Sterrett, *U.S. Geological Survey*, 186.

While this transaction was profitable to Thomas and Wood, that was not the case for the ATC. In the 1898 *Report of the Governor of New Mexico to the Secretary of the Interior*, we find the following:

> There are other properties in the Little Hatchet Mountains near the camp of Hachita which a few years ago were profitably worked but at the present writing reliable data is not obtainable. It is known for a fact, however, that stones to the value of $20,000 have been extracted and that valuable stones are frequently encountered, but their extent is not generally known to the world at large.[10]

The value of the turquoise mined would have met only the payment price for the five claims. The 7 percent gross commission on turquoise mined from all ATC properties was yet another example of the financial mismanagement plaguing the ATC. At the time this contract was signed, prospects appeared bright for the ATC to achieve its goal of dominance in the turquoise market.

Yet optimistic forecasts do not pay the bills, and the ATC had many liabilities beginning with $250,000 in bonds that Farmers' Loan and Trust Company of New York had issued and sold to investors. Doty was agent for the ATC and was responsible for negotiating the purchase and terms of the Hachita mines, although he may have been less than enthusiastic and was overruled by President John Andrews, who had demonstrated poor business judgment in his other affairs.

A letter from Doty to his wife Cora, written in January 1896 when he was in Hachita overseeing mining activity, shows his disappointment in the investment:

I had a telegram from George[11] today which I judge was sent as soon as they received my last shipment. I understand perfectly well what that contained and etc. At the same time I know what I am trying to accomplish here, and more I never expected to find as good stone here as we get at Cerrillos, but I do think I shall be able to get, and very soon, a large quantity of stone that will be marketable. In fact I can't imagine why they should have sent me such a telegram as they did today saying they were tired of Grant County and etc. From the style of it I should think they expected me to go out with a saw and cut one of the ledges in two in the morning and be able to let them know just what it contained by night instead of which if I am able to cut three or four feet a day with the force I have employed. They are doing a lot of work and then the stones have to be picked out of the solid rock one at a time. If I could give the All Mighty an order and have them made just as we want them, I would have sent several barrels long ago and then no one would have cared to buy them as they would be so plenty that no one would want them. But I won't be here much longer as I have about finished up the assessment work and got about everything out of the Herbert mine that is in sight without opening up a lot of new ground and that I don't care to do in the present state of affairs. So I shall soon leave for Cerrillos where I am sure of results but while I am here I intend to know all about this property.[12]

Doty corresponded often with Cora during this stay in Hachita. His attitude of the prospects of other mines in the district and a falling out with Thomas and Wood was evident in the following letter:

If Thomas and Wood should offer to sell me the Woodbert mine for $25 today I would laugh at them. Since Wood has been away I have had it thoroughly inspected and I don't think they even got a salable stone out of it. I can't say but I don't think I will be here more than a week longer for by that time I shall have done all the outside work I want to do, and I don't propose to open up anything for Thomas and Wood to gobble up if they succeed in getting possession.[13]

Although Doty appears uninterested in pursuing any claims in Hachita, it is interesting to hear in another letter around the same time that he had made a claim in his wife's name in the area:

I have located a mine here in your name and shall call it the Cora Mine. I have been working it the last few days and have almost got the ledge cut through. I have found plenty of colors and they are more like the Cerrillos property than anything we have opened up yet. The rock is harder and it's the largest ledge in the camp and more it's in the north side of the Hill and is a continuation of the Herbert which is the only place we have had any satisfactory stone from as yet. The stone or rather colors can be traced on this ledge on the surface for nearly 300 feet. I shall do work enough on it to get some idea of what it contains and also be able to hold it until January 1, 98. I hope this will put us in a position to be a little independent but can't tell yet. I expect during this week or the first of next to send George some stone and I will then see what they think of them. I have taken out a lot of them all ready but they are within a few feet of the surface and there is nothing yet worth shipping.[14]

Doty's letter indicates he was well aware of the financial difficulties of the ATC and was trying to hedge his bets by putting the claim in Cora's name to not be available to his creditors and to move Thomas and Wood out of the picture as middle men. The claim was not developed and eventually passed to the ATC.

H.H. Topakyan of New York, rug merchant and representative for the Shah of Iran, had claims in the Eureka District near old Hachita in addition to those he had in the Cerrillos District. He had three claims about one and one half miles west of the residence of Sterling Burwell, a well-known local prospector and miner. The Persian, Kevorkian, and Topakyan claims were located between November 9 and November 11, 1894 by Henry R. Ewalt of Grant County, New Mexico. The names of the claims indicate that Ewalt was acting as agent for Topakyan, and on November 21, 1894 the claims were transferred to him. He also purchased claims in the Burro Mountain District. In a deed dated July 18, 1894 H.H. Topakyan purchased from James Winters for the amount of $700 the San Pedro and California turquoise claims.

His involvement in Cerrillos, the Burros, and Hachita is best remembered as an example of the popularity of turquoise at the time and how there were many smaller players locating claims and attempting to enter the turquoise marketplace. Few would achieve the level of success of the major operators. In this instance it appears, from the timing of these claims—which are about the same time as his claims he obtained from Mike O'Neil in Cerrillos—that Topakyan was obtaining claims in the same areas in which the ATC and the Azure Mining Company were operating in a rather blatant attempt to duplicate their success. It is uncertain how long Topakyan maintained these claims but if his experience at Cerrillos is any indication, he was more committed to the idea of mining turquoise than he was to the practical application of actually operating a mine.

By 1897 it had become clear that neither the quantity nor quality of Hachita turquoise was going to warrant serious investment of time and money. As noted, the area was remote and the conditions harsh with little water or transport as the nearest train line at the time was over 40 miles away. That did not deter the efforts of many to continue to locate and file claims. Although they may have been turquoise claims, they could well have been for metal. Following the sale of the Aztec and Montezuma claims to Wood and Thomas on April 27, 1893, Young and Thetge still controlled the Idaho, King Solomon, and Turquoise 1 and 2 claims. On April 30, 1893, just three days after the transfer of the Aztec and Montezuma, the Turquoise Central claim was located on the eastern boundary of the Montezuma in the names of Young, Thetge, and John L. Dean.[15] This was followed in January of 1894 by the location of the Mystery about two miles southwest of the King mine, about three-quarters of a mile from Halfway Hill, and one and a half miles west of the U.S. mineral deposit marker. This time Young was in partnership with George W. Miles.[16] At some time before December 10, 1894, the Lady Franklin had been located with Young as the owner, but he evidently allowed that claim to lapse and it was absent from the proof of labor report for 1897.

On January 20, 1897, the Ladies Choice Gem and Aztec Gem were located by Young with George D. Arnold and Clifton W. Arnold of Cerrillos. It was located one mile west of the King mine and one and a half miles northwest of the U.S. mineral market.[17] It was included in a group of claims offered to

Howard Clark of Halifax, Nova Scotia on February 2, 1897 by Young and the Arnolds for $40,000, if paid on or before July 1, 1897.[18] The sale must not have been completed as the group is included in a proof of labor assessment filing for the year 1899.[19] On the same day, Thetge transferred his half interest in Turquoise No. 1 and 2, Idaho and King Solomon, and one-third interest in the Turquoise Central to A.C. Young for $500.[20] Although Young and his new partners appeared to continue to be optimistic about the value of turquoise mining in the Hachitas, Thetge had decided to sell out completely.

M.W. Porterfield, with his partner, George W. Robinson of Pueblo, Colorado, who owned diverse mining interests including those in the Silver City area, made some of the last claims in the area before the end of the turquoise boom. Porterfield evidently was still attempting to make his mark in the turquoise trade. He had been very successful at promoting turquoise for the territory, though the trade never achieved the level of commercial success he desired. Porterfield was given half interest in the claims for financial assistance, and operated them in 1909.[21] His claims in the Eureka district came during a time when the demand for turquoise was falling. What turquoise he did find was generally poor quality and would not have been desirable even during the boom years of the mid to late 90s.

Robinson and Porterfield Turquoise Mountain Azure claim.
D.B. Sterrett, *U.S. Geological Survey*, 178.

Robinson and Porterfield's Aztec claim was located on June 4, 1908.[22] It was situated about one and a half miles south of Turquoise Mountain on the northeastern slope of Howell's Ridge, 500 feet below its rim,[23] and was a relocation of the ATC's Aztec claim, which, based on the POL assessment they had filed for the year 1906, had been abandoned a short time before.[24] At some point, Harry Wood ran a tunnel under the existing prehistoric workings, and Robinson later opened new diggings above the Wood Tunnel south of the old Indian diggings. Detailed accounts relate that the claim's mineral composition, although valued, would have been more useful for the higher quality turquoise in the Muñiz in Cerrillos and the Azure in the Burro Mountains. The deposit was in jarositized sandstone and diorite, closely resembling decomposed jarositized sodic facies of monzonite. The turquoise associated with limonite stains filled pronounced joints and formed nuggets in both trachyte leads and isolated areas, with the nuggets generally being of better quality than the vein material. Overall, the grade of turquoise tended to be softer and paler than that from the more northern areas, and some material that had good color when first mined soon faded upon drying.[25]

In addition to the Aztec, Robinson and Porterfield filed claims on the Cameo, the Galilee, and the Azure. It is interesting to find a detailed report by Sterrett in the 1909 *MRUS*. Although we know the turquoise boom was almost over, that was not at all evident to those operating the mines. Regarding work on the Azure, he reported one working at the northeast end of Turquoise Mountain and another one near the middle of the hill. He mentioned remains of ancient Indian mining activities that he attributed to Aztecs. Most importantly was his report that Robinson, who from all indications was responsible for most of the work we see in photos of the period, had dug a tunnel about 160 feet long that connected with an open cut on the surface. This indicated substantial mining activity. Sterrett went on to describe the turquoise found in the Azure saying the matrix was harder and formed beautiful matrix gems ranging in color from dark sky blue to pale blue and greenish blue. Sadly, for all their efforts, this was too little too late.

Robinson and his daughter at cabin at the Azure.
D.B. Sterrett, *U.S. Geological Survey*, 179.

Robinson and his daughter in the old Indian workings on the Azure claim; filling of
waste rock in old stope above them. D.B. Sterrett, *U.S. Geological Survey*, 180.

George Robinson at the Cameo claim. D.B. Sterrett, *U.S. Geological Survey*, 183.

The Jarilla Mountains were first mined for copper ore in the late 1870s, but the remoteness of the area created problems for both mining and transportation, and interest waned. In March 1892, William E. Hidden, who owned the Emerald and Hiddenite Mining Company and had discovered hiddenite, prospected for turquoise throughout New Mexico. He briefly stopped in the Burro Mountain region. An article in *The Jewelers Circular* mentioned that at least 50 kilograms of "pure" non-matrix, sky blue turquoise had been shipped during the 12 months prior to his visit and that the origin was not in the area of the historic Indian diggings, but in the Cows Springs district, operated by the Azure Mining Company.[26] Hidden certainly would have been aware of these activities because at that time he was well acquainted with both Gyulo Armeny and Lippman Tannenbaum, who had leased the hiddenite and emerald mine his company owned. He stopped in Hachita for eight weeks, opening up some of the old Indian diggings, but decided to abandon the area because he found little high-grade turquoise.

Hidden continued on to the Jarilla Mountains, about 50 miles northeast of El Paso and about the same distance east of Las Cruces. He described the extreme remoteness of the area—the nearest rail line was in those cities and the near-absence of water required transporting it as well as all other supplies. He described at least 10 locations the Indians had worked, referencing not only stone hammers and pottery fragments he found, but also shallow trenches and holes with long overgrown piled debris rock that evidenced their age. Mathien cited references stating these diggings were made between A.D. 1150 and 1400 during several phases of occupation, with emphasis shifting from agriculture to mining because of decreased rainfall.[27] In spite of the remote location, Hidden built a house from timber hauled 30 miles from the Organ Mountains. He also discovered turquoise. Regarding the ancient diggings, Hidden said:

> The Mexicans believe that both the Pueblos and ancient Aztecs worked these mines for turquoise. It is true today that Pueblos value turquoise, which they term "shoo ar me," even more than the Navajos. The Apache name for it is "steh" but they care little for it. The Mexicans call it "char-chu-a-tey" which calls to mind the Aztec "chal-chi-hui-tl" of many authors.[28]

Hidden filed his claim in the names of Lippman Tannenbaum, the Block brothers, and himself, although he retained only a small interest. This indicates he may well have been scouting for turquoise claims for Tannenbaum the entire trip. He named the claim the Shoo-ar-me. This gave Tannenbaum the turquoise mine he felt he had been denied by his partner Armeny in the Burros. Hidden stated he worked the mine for six months, "discovering" at least 50 kilograms of turquoise "some of which found a ready market in New York and London."[29] He appeared to be optimistic about the prospect of discovering turquoise "as beautiful and as large as the world has yet seen" and declared that, in spite of the remoteness of the area and proximity to the Mescalero Apache reservation, the mines would be "energetically worked as time and the seasons permit." Evidently neither time nor the seasons cooperated because little if any turquoise was mined in the area for several years and, when it resumed, it was not by Hidden or his partners. Also it is unlikely that Tannenbaum and Hidden remained on good terms because Armeny and Tannenbaum backed out of the lease on Hidden's mine and he sued them.

Murder in the Mountains

Amos J. DeMeules was an early riser. He had worked hard over the prior 11 years since moving to Las Cruces from Santa Fe following his army service in Colorado. He had come far from his humble beginnings in Genesee County, New York. With a French Canadian heritage, DeMeules had looked for his future in the West and the army was his ticket out. A barber by trade, he longed for success on a grand scale and now it appeared he was on the cusp of achieving his dream. It was November 28, 1898, and DeMeules had accumulated several claims in the Jarilla Mountains. In one mine he had discovered gold ore that, although assayed as low-grade, was of sufficient quantity to yield him a healthy profit. In addition to that, some claims included deposits of copper ore and the completion of the El Paso and Southwestern rail line gave easy access to the ore smelters in El Paso, overcoming the limitations posed by the Jarillas.

DeMeules located a remote turquoise mine that had been abandoned. He held on to the claim by doing his assessment work and making a living as best he could. He financed much of his investment in his mining ventures by persuading J.A. Baird, a wealthy resident of El Paso, to finance his efforts. Baird was rewarded for his faith when Amos shipped, over a two-year period, thousands of dollars' worth of turquoise to buyers in New York and elsewhere, including to the largest and most well-known, Tiffany and Co. One shipment to that firm exceeded $10,000. This turquoise quality was highly regarded, and A.H. Richards, a well-known El Paso jeweler, hosted an exhibition of De-Meules' turquoise, including one stone reported to be the largest ever cut in the United States.[30] In addition to the prospects of his claims and the success of the turquoise mine, he also optioned an interest in many of his claims for $15,000 to John A. Eddy, who with his brother John was making a major investment in the Jarillas. DeMeules had certainly sweetened the pot by including in the deal the location of the only permanent water source in the Jarillas.[31]

DeMeules' success came from working long hours and facing down those who tried to take from him what he had worked so hard to build. Claim jumpers were common, and a dispute over one of his claims had required him to post armed guards at the mine. One of those guards was Jacobo Flores, a Mexican from Las Cruces who had been working for him for two years, presumably as a miner. That November morning when DeMeules was eating breakfast in his house at the mine, Flores approached him and demanded $29 in back pay. Whatever his reason, DeMeules became angry and refused. As he rose from his seat, Flores pulled a revolver and shot him once in the head, breaking his neck and killing him instantly. In a statement given through an interpreter to an *El Paso Daily Times* reporter in the county jail where he was held after the shooting, Flores recounted:

I am a poor man and have five brothers to feed. DeMeules owed me $29, which I wanted to take to Las Cruces to my brothers. Two days ago I asked him for this money, but he would not give it to me for fear that I would go away and not work for him any longer. So today when I went into his kitchen where he was eating and asked him for the money again DeMeules became very angry and began to scold me and throw things about and this frightened me and I thought I might get hurt and so I pulled out my pistol and shot him. DeMeules had no gun but I always carry one; still I did not go in there to shoot him but determined to get my money as my brothers are hungry. I did not try to run away, as they say, but they took hold of me and brought me here, and that is all I know.[32]

On October 16,1899, Jacobo Flores pleaded guilty to murder in the second degree of A.J. DeMeules, the Turquoise King of the Jarilla Mountains, and was sentenced to 21 years in prison.[33] Less than a month before, Germain DeMeules, Amos' father and sole heir, had deeded to John A. Eddy most of the DeMeules claims for payment of $17,000. The dreams and ambitions of Amos DeMeules had reached the end.[34]

Jacobo Flores escaped from the penitentiary in Las Vegas, NM on July 9, 1905. He was captured and returned to prison September 15, 1905. On April 4, 1910, he escaped a second time from the Silver City Camp. We have no record of his recapture, or whether he served the remainder of his sentence.

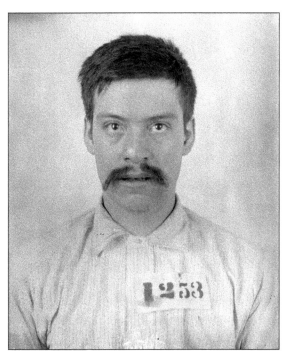

Jacobo Flores. New Mexico Department of Corrections, New Mexico State Records Center and Archives, negative number 1253.

At the time DeMeules was mining turquoise and shipping to New York with such promise, others were active in the area. In the 1913 edition of *MRUS*, Sterrett describes the turquoise deposits of the Jarilla mining district as occurring in two groups, about two miles and four miles, respectively, northwest of Oro Grande about 60 miles northeast of El Paso. He places one group just west of Brice, a post office off a spur of the El Paso and Southwestern Railroad running through Oro Grande, and the other about two miles north of Brice. The turquoise deposits in the northern group included the DeMeules mine and the Laura claim of F.B. Stuart of El Paso. In the southern group were the Alabama claims, locally known as Tiffany, and the claim of Luna, Moreno, and Ascarate. The DeMeules mine was leased by Cy Ryan and Tom Kelly, presumably from John Eddy, and continued to yield what Sterrett described as "a large quantity of good turquoise." Also, the Luna, Moreno, and Ascarate claim was worked around 1900.[35] In 1901 it was reported that the DeMeules mines had been sold to T.A. and P.A. Kelley for $32,000 and were being mined for copper ore.[37]

Luna, Moreno, and Ascarate turquoise mine. D.B. Sterrett, 559 1913. *U.S. Geological Survey.*

A.D. Hudson at end of cut of Luna, Moreno, and Ascarate turquoise mine. Hudson was associated with the Texas Turquoise Company out of El Paso that operated in the Van Horn Texas area with little success, July 1913.
D.B. Sterrett, *U.S. Geological Survey*, 560.

In our Great American Turquoise Rush narrative, we have seen several instances of mines with the name Tiffany. The Jarillas were no exception. Although we have reports of shipments of turquoise to Tiffany, no evidence exists that either the man or the firm owned any turquoise claims—local miners perpetrated this myth in their desire to attach the brand name recognition to their claims. Sterrett mentioned that the Tiffany mine had been patented under the name of the Alabama claims.[37] Pat Garrett, the former sheriff of Lincoln County who killed Billy the Kid, was renowned for his lack of dependability. He had tried his hand at several business ventures with little success. In 1899 he, along with W. H.H. and Clinton B. Llewelyn, formed the Alabama Gold and Copper Mining Company, with the objective of owning and operating gold and copper mines in the Oro Grande area. Their intent appeared less to prospect and extract minerals than it was to peddle stock to investors and pocket the proceeds, and the company disbanded two years later.[38] The Alabama claim was the original location of the Shoo-ar-me claim and most probably the Tiffany name association was because of Tannenbaum, who was incorrectly associated with the Tiffany organization in other areas, lending the Tiffany name falsely to other turquoise mines. Perhaps that association fit the purpose of Garrett and the Llewelyn as well. Although the 1901 *New Mexico Mines and Minerals Report* stated Llewellyn and Garrett were working "profitable" turquoise mines in the area, no other record shows they were active in that endeavor.

Part of the so-called Tiffany turquoise mine (Alabama group); 2.5 miles northwest of Orogrande, looking east of south from dump of Luna, Moreno, and Ascarate turquoise mines. Open cut and deep shaft on hillside to left. Other workings on extreme right in gap. D.B. Sterrett, *U.S. Geological Survey*, July 1913, 561.

In his report, Sterrett also described the quality of turquoise found during the period following the death of Amos DeMeules. Regarding the DeMeules mine, he stated, "Turquoise of various grades was found ranging from pale blue to dark blue, bluish green, and green. Very pretty matrix was observed, in which the turquoise was mottled with irregular patches of limonite and limonite-stained quartz in the veinlets." He continued that at the Tiffany mine, "Beautiful matrix could be cut from some of the veinlets." Regarding the Laura claim, he said, "There was much turquoise suitable for matrix, which would yield gems of good blue handsomely mottled with brown limonite stains."[39]

DeMeules turquoise mine with mine dumps in front of cabin. D.B. Sterrett, *U.S. Geological Survey*, July 1913, 557.

DeMeules cabin. This may be the possible site of his murder in 1898. A.D. Hudson is in the photo and was probably serving as Sterrett's guide. D.B. Sterrett, *U.S. Geological Survey*, July 1913, 558.

This report is another instance we see of consideration of matrix in turquoise as "gem" material of high grade. Before only the non-matrix, sky blue was considered for purchase by east coast buyers. By the end of the first decade of the new century, turquoise tastes were moving towards appreciation of matrix as well as the more traditional clear blue that had been the standard set by Persian turquoise. This is demonstrated in the following advertisement from the *American Monthly Review of Reviews,* published sometime around the 1904 Louis and Clark Exposition, St. Louis. George Bell was a well-known lapidary from Denver who had cut for many mines, including the Azure Mine in the Burros. He was listed as a vendor at the St. Louis Exposition.

Sadly for the turquoise business, just as interest was beginning to develop beyond the narrow appreciation of what was considered high-grade turquoise, the country was beset by the financial collapse of 1907 and the resulting recession of 1908. This, combined with changing trends in the jewelry market, brought to a halt any substantial demand for turquoise. When the market began to rebound in the 1920s, it was beautiful turquoise in matrix set in handmade American Indian jewelry that established the demand in southwest Indian art that continues to the present.

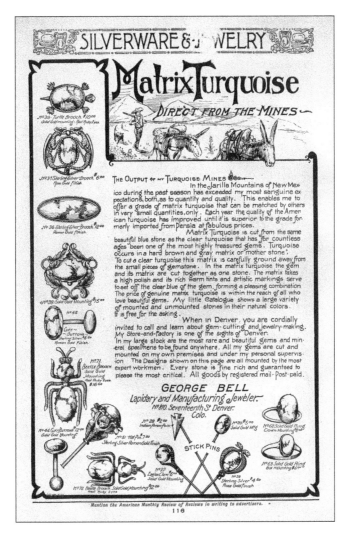

George Bell advertisement. *American Monthly Review of Reviews*, December 1901.

Notes

1. D.B. Sterrett, *Mineral Resources of the United States, 1909, Part 2*, 791.
2. *Grant County Mining Records Book 14*, 296–298.
3. W.E. Hidden, "New Mines of Turquoise in New Mexico," *The Jewelers Circular*, Nov. 1, 1893, 44.
4. *Grant County Mining Deeds Book 27*, 349–350.
5. *Grant County Mining Records Book 15*, 247–250.
6. Ibid., 254.

7. D.B. Sterrett, *Mineral Resources of the United States, 1909, Part 2,* 794, and Grant County Book of Mining Locations 15, 253–254.
8. *Grant County Mining Records Book 15,* 401.
9. *Grant County Mining Records Book 15,* 247–248.
10. *Report of the Governor of New Mexico,* 1898, 216.
11. Probably George Kuntz, the chief gemologist of Tiffany and Co. at the time. Doty was the agent for the ATC and responsible of selling the turquoise. He had close ties to Tiffany and Co., the largest purchaser of turquoise at the time, and was known to have bought much of the output from the ATC. Kuntz, as chief gemologist, would have been responsible for reviewing the quality of turquoise purchased.
12. Arizona Historical Society, Doty letter to wife Cora, January 1896, MS 840, Wales Papers, 1844–1896.
13. Ibid.
14. Ibid.
15. *Grant County Mining Records Book 15,* 403–404.
16. Ibid., 503.
17. Ibid., 16, 223–554.
18. *Grant County Mining Records Book 33,* 551.
19. Ibid., Book 38, 119.
20. Ibid., Book 33, p. 561.
21. D.B. Sterrett, *Mineral Resources of the United States, 1909, Part 2,* 792.
22. *Grant County Mining Records Book 25,* 140.
23. D.B. Sterrett, *Mineral Resources of the United States, 1909, Part 2,* 793–794.
24. *Grant County Mining Location Book 25,* 340–341.
25. D.B. Sterrett, *Mineral Resources of the United States, 1909, Part 2,* 794, and Lasky, 1947, 82.
26. W.E. Hidden, "New Mines of Turquoise in New Mexico," *The Jewelers Circular,* November 1, 1893, 44.
27. F.J. Mathien, "Evidence of Prehistoric Turquoise Mining at Orogrande, Jarilla Mountains, New Mexico," "Of Potts and Rocks," papers in honor of A. Helen Warren, Archeological Society of New Mexico, 1995.
28. Hidden, p. 41.
29. Ibid.
30. *Silver City Enterprise,* 12/02/1898 article.
31. Furman, J., "Basin's Belongings: Miners hit Jarilla Mountains," *Alamogordo Daily News,* January 3, 2004.
32. *El Paso Daily Times,* Tuesday, November 29, 1898.
33. *Socorro Chieftain,* October 20, 1899.
34. *Otero County Mining Deed Records, Book 10,* 46.
35. D.B. Sterrett, *Mineral Resources of the United States, Part 2,* 1913, 699.
36. *Mines and Minerals of New Mexico, 1901,* 112.
37. D.B. Sterrett, *Mineral Resources of the United States, Part 2,* 1913, 700.
38. W.C. Jameson, *Pat Garrett: The Man Behind the Badge,* Boulder: Taylor Trade Publishing, 2015, 170.
39. D.B. Sterrett, *Mineral Resources of the United States, Part 2,* 1913, 701.

Arizona

5

Courtland

Of all the areas mined during The Great American Turquoise Rush, none played such an important role, yet remained as unknown as Turquoise Mountain near Courtland Arizona. Courtland lies sixteen miles due east of Tombstone, Arizona. More importantly for our narrative, it is about 150 miles overland from the turquoise claims of the Burro Mountains in New Mexico.

An employee of the Sonora Mining Company of New York, Fred Brunckow, made the first mineral strike near present day Tombstone in Cochise County, Arizona in 1857 when discoveries of gold and silver in California and Nevada motivated exploration throughout the West. Unfortunately for Brunckow, conditions for developing a mining operation in the Arizona Territory of 1857 were difficult, and he was murdered. Mining operations did not return to the area until the late 1870s as control of the area shifted away from Apaches and Mexican bandits. In 1877, Edward Schieffelin, with his brother Albert and their partner Richard Gird, discovered the Lucky Cuss and Toughnut ore deposits. In 1880, the brothers sold their interest in the properties for $600,000 (over $14MM in current value) and a year later Gird sold his for even more money, although it is reported that, being a gentleman, he split the difference with his former partners.[1] They were among the few to make a fortune in Tombstone before water shortage and depleting ore production ended the boom.

The first mention of turquoise in the area was once again by William P. Blake, who in 1882 reported about ancient turquoise mines he called Turquois Mountain:

> At the turquois locality there are two or more ancient excavations upon the south face of the mountain and large piles of waste or debris thrown out are overgrown with century plants, yuccas and *Cactaceae* (cacti). It has not been worked in a long time and probably never by the Apache.

The excavations are not as extensive as at Los Cerrillos and it is more difficult to find specimens of the mineral.[2]

The Turquoise mining district was formed around the late 1870s, most likely named as such because of signs of early Indian turquoise mining activities. The Great American Turquoise Rush was driven by many people performing different services. Some located turquoise claims, while others managed and operated the mines. Others were responsible for processing the rough turquoise and selling a finished product to the jewelry trade. The intent of investors in each of the geographic areas was to gain control of every aspect of this process. Of all of those who participated in the effort to locate the turquoise claims, no one had a greater influence on the development of successful turquoise operations than Nicholas C. Rascom. His obituary from the *Silver City Enterprise* of May 7, 1909 presents a solid picture of the man:

> Deceased was quiet and unassuming and was typical of the taciturn, steady, determined man of the mountains, ever searching for mineral wealth, a type to whom the west owes a debt it can never repay and a type that is fast disappearing with the onrush of eastern civilization. He is reported to have located more mining claims and sunk more prospect holes than any man in the southwest.

Rascom had first entered the Courtland Gleeson district in 1878 or 1879, and from the beginning had focused his attention on turquoise claims. Although Smith stated that Henry Durant made the first turquoise claim in Courtland then sold to Rascom and Tannenbaum,[3] we will see that this is incorrect and perhaps came from confusion with S.H. Bryant, who filed some early claims with Rascom. To understand the development of Turquoise Mountain at Courtland, it is necessary to track the development of the turquoise mines in the Burro Mountains of New Mexico.

Nicholas C. Rascom, Courtesy of Palace of the Governors Photo Archives (NMHM/DCA) negative 50555.

The central theme of our narrative is to demonstrate how, during The Great American Turquoise Rush, competing interests—primarily from the New York jewelry trade—sought to establish dominance in the southwest turquoise market by creating a cartel, or monopoly, that could then control both supply and price. We have seen how the ATC attempted to control the market around Cerrillos and expand into Hachita. Their main competitor was the Azure Mining Company operating in the Burro Mountains near Silver City, NM, and what would become Tyrone, NM.

As the market for turquoise exploded in 1892 following Kunz's announcement, exploration increased throughout the areas known to have old turquoise mines that Ancestral Pueblo Indians and others had worked. After partnering with Tannenbaum and Hidden in Hidden's emerald and hiddenite mine in North Carolina, Gyulo Armeny was interested in expanding into the turquoise market. As noted in Chapter 3, he had worked closely with Rascom in obtaining the claims transferred to the newly formed Azure Mining Company in the fall of 1891. The claims were purchased from Rascom and Porterfield in August 1891. Rascom had also located claims with Armeny, which were transferred to the Azure Mining Company.

Armeny and Tannenbaum had broken the lease on the Hidden emerald mine because it did not live up to their expectations. Hidden later sued them for that breach of contract. At that time, they agreed to be mutually included in whatever opportunity the other might initiate. As Armeny was locating claims and securing deeds to other claims in the Burros during early 1891, he offered Tannenbaum the option of entering into a business arrangement for developing the turquoise mines. As we know, Tannenbaum declined and the Azure Mining Company was formed. Although not immediate, the success of the mines grew, with sales of several thousand dollars during the first year of operation, but not to the extent they became with the discovery of the Elizabeth Pocket in 1893. Tannenbaum's claim that Armeny had purposely deceived him by providing him with chalky turquoise resulted in a lawsuit that began in 1892, reached the New York State Supreme Court, and in November 1894 judgment was made for Tannenbaum, the effects of which would affect Armeny and Tannenbaum's relationship for years.

As the case was proceeding through the courts, the hunt was on for turquoise claims. As in every instance where turquoise claims were developed during that time, they occurred at ancient Indian turquoise mines. This was true when W.E. Hidden, in partnership with Tannenbaum, established the Sho-ar-me claim in the Jarilla Mountains, which he worked for several months in 1892.

This was also true for Rascom who, following his sale of claims in the Burro Mountains to Armeny in 1891, returned to the Courtland, Arizona area in search of new turquoise claims. On February 23, 1892, Rascom, with S.H. Bryant, located the Azure claim which is a common name for a turquoise mine but also may indicate for whom Rascom was working. They located the Turquoise claim on the same day, and on February 24 they located the Asia claim. The location by Bryant and Armeny of the Nightingale mine on March 29, 1892—witnessed by Mabel Bryant, presumably the wife of S.H. Bryant who gave his address as Cochise County and was probably a local miner known to Rascom—demonstrated Rascom's continuing association with Armeny. On April 2, 1892, Armeny and Bryant located the Carrie claim, and on June 7 they located the Lillie claim. Each of these filings was witnessed by Rascom. Since there is no record of any claims made in the name of Henry Durant, we conclude this person is actually S.H. Bryant.

It did not take long for Armeny's intentions to become clear. On March 31, 1892, Rascom deeded his half interest in the Turquoise, Azure, and Asia claims to Armeny for $5,000. On June 7, 1892, Bryant deeded his half interest in the Turquoise, Azure, Asia, Nightingale, Carrie, and Lillie claims to Armeny for $1,000. The premium paid to Rascom may indicate he was working as an agent for Armeny in obtaining these claims. The following day, June 8, Armeny deeded the Turquoise, Azure, Asia, Nightingale, Carrie, and Lillie claims to Adam Herlich for $200. This is the same Adam Herlich who had located the Blue Bell with Mike O'Neil in the Cerrillos Hills in January of 1892 and exchanged his half interest with O'Neil later in the year for half interest in the Shah, which was on Turquoise Hill near the claims of the ATC. The previous day, June 7, Armeny had deeded to Herlich the George, which he had located on April 4, 1892, and the Julia, located on June 6, 1892, for $1. Comparing the difference between the amount Armeny paid for these claims and the amount he received in the sale to Herlich, it is clear Herlich was not a disinterested third party in the transaction.

The Herlich family was well known to Armeny. According to the 1880 census, Peter Herlich, age 61, worked as a printer at a card factory and lived in a two-story home with his wife Elizabeth, 60, and his two unmarried sons, Adam, 28, who worked as a jeweler's assistant, and his brother George, 23, a day laborer. The Herlichs rented part of their home to Armeny and his wife Kate, both age 30, and their three daughters Lily, 6, Caroline, 5, and Julie, 3. Armeny worked in a jewelry shop, possibly with Adam Herlich. It is reasonable to assume that as Armeny's career developed and he prospered, he continued his relationship with one of his oldest friends. It is also possible that Herlich was Kate Armeny's brother and thus Armeny's brother-in-law. Many of the Armenys and Herlichs are buried together in Woodlawn Cemetery in the Bronx, indicating a family relationship. Susan Marie Armeny, Armeny's granddaughter whose father was Armeny's son from his second marriage, related in correspondence with Philip Chambless that in 2003 her mother still owned the George mine, which was supposedly named for Armeny's son from his first marriage. Certainly the Julia and the Lillie could have been named for his daughters.

Adam Herlich did not enjoy the ownership of his turquoise mines for long. On July 6, 1892, he deeded to Armeny's partners Louis Kahn and Meyer D. Rothschild, officers in the Azure Mining Company, the Turquoise, Azure, Asia, Nightingale, Carrie, and Lillie mines for the amount of $2,000. Why did Armeny find it necessary not to have a direct transaction between his partners and himself? Perhaps the pending lawsuit with Tannenbaum drove his decision to keep assets out of his name, should the case go against him, which it did. The result was that, by the middle of 1892, principles of the Azure

Mining Company controlled turquoise mines in the Burros and Courtland, and Armeny had realized a loss, for accounting purposes, on the transactions. Herlich also played a role in Cerrillos.

As noted in Chapter 2, competing interests, primarily the ATC and the New Mexico Turquoise Company, fought for control of the turquoise market in Cerrillos. O'Neil was not only involved with the New Mexico Turquoise Company as superintendent at the Persian, but also invested in other turquoise claims he had, including the Blue Bell, obtained from Herlich on July 26, 1892. If Herlich had been acting as an agent for Armeny in the Cerrillos, then his location of the Blue Bell indicated that Armeny was also looking to establish properties in Cerrillos at the same time he was locating properties in the Burro Mountains in 1891. Herlich had located the Blue Bell with Mike O'Neil earlier in the year and traded his half interest to O'Neil for half interest in the Shah sometime later in 1892. Following the transfer of the Courtland claims to the Kahn brothers and Rothschild in July, perhaps the exchange was made for Herlich to position himself and the Azure Mining Company—if he were acting as agent—right in the backyard of the ATC.

It is probably no coincidence that following the acquisition of the additional claims in Courtland and the location of the claims in Cerrillos by Herlich and O'Neil, the ATC felt compelled to expand the scope of their operations. In May 1893, they purchased the Hachita claims from Thomas and Wood as described in Chapter 4. The terms of this transaction had a severe negative impact on the finances of the ATC, because they agreed to a very high royalty payment to Thomas and Wood. This most likely was the result of what the company felt was an imperative to match the Azure Mining Company's property development. By the spring of 1893, each of these companies controlled claims throughout New Mexico and Arizona.

Looking northwest towards Turquoise Mountain one mile northwest of Courtland Arizona. The turquoise openings begin in the summit in the quartzite ledge and extend a half mile north (to the right) along each side of the ridge. D.B. Sterrett, July, 1913, *U.S. Geological Survey*, 562.

Looking northeast towards Turquoise Mountain with several dumps of turquoise workings along the mountainside.
D.B. Sterrett, July, 1913, *U.S. Geological Survey*, 565.

Looking north along the summit of Turquoise Mountain. The ridge is formed by quartzite and small workings may be seen in the foreground. D.B. Sterrett, July, 1913, *U.S. Geological Survey*, 563.

Two tunnels in an open cut on the west side of Turquoise Mountain near the north end. D.B. Sterrett, July 1913, *U.S. Geological Survey,*, 564.

Turquoise production for the Azure Mining Company in the Burro Mountains suffered a slow start. According to Jacobson, the first seven months of production paid only the expenses. If the company had commenced production right after acquiring the claims, this would have been November 1891 to June 1892. This explains the company's desire to acquire the additional claims in Courtland—they wanted a backup source for turquoise should their Burro claims not produce. This was not the case and, with the discovery of the Elizabeth Pocket, production increased significantly. Jacobson, quoting Kunz, reported in 1893 they increased revenues to $50,000.[4]

At this point, though we can follow the movement of the various mines through the location notices and mining deeds, we must speculate as to motivation. We know Tannenbaum filed suit against Armeny in 1892, for interest in any profits Armeny received from the Azure Mining Company's Azure mine.

As production increased in the Burros, the Azure Mining Company's need to maintain its Courtland properties lessened. Newspaper accounts from the time confirm this, including the following: "N.C. Rascom, manager of the Armeny turquoise mines in the Turquois district, was in town today. He reports the mines looking most promising."[5]

On February 4, 1894, Armeny deeded to Rascom the Catalonia, Montezuma, Penzance, and Albion claims for $1. Two reasons explain why the deed of sale was recorded in this amount: The parties wish to avoid any public record of the amount of the transaction and an additional payment is made off the books; or one of the parties is acting as agent for the other. The long history of Rascom and Armeny indicates Rascom was continuing his business relationship with Armeny and his partners.

As the Azure Mining Company operations decreased at Turquoise Mountain, Rascom became active in locating and accumulating claims. On January 1, 1895, he located the Peerless. On January 2 he located the Minola, and on January 8 he located the Avalon. On February 25, the Prince was located and February 28, the Helen. On July 29, 1895, William Holmes, who may have been a prospecting partner with Rascom, deeded to Rascom his half interest in the Last Chance, Chicago, Turquoise Queen, Inez, Gold Bug, Alabama, and Germania. Rascom was doing what he did best—locating and accumulating claims.

On April 26, 1895, Rascom deeded to Lippman Tannenbaum the Julia, Penzance, Minola, Prince, Highland, Gem, Colon, and Helen claims for $1 each. There are three explanations: (1) Rascom was feeling charitable (not!); (2) there was a side deal; or (3) he was acting on behalf of a third party in facilitating the transaction. Of the three, under the circumstances it is not unreasonable to conclude this arrangement may have been a way for Armeny to placate his old partner. Tannenbaum was litigious to a high degree. Perhaps his entering Courtland at the same time Armeny and the Azure Mining Company were focusing their attention on the highly profitable Burro Mountains claims were related in some way.

Kahn and Rothschild continued to maintain a presence at Courtland, though not actively developing the claims as they had done previously with Rascom supervising. On December 10 and 11, 1895, they recorded supplemental notice of locations for the Nightingale, Lillie, Carrie, Asia, Azure, and Turquoise claims that had been the original claims purchased from Armeny through Herlich. At the same time, Herlich made a supplemental notice of location for the George. Although these claims were recorded as a supplemental location at the Cochise County Recorder, this would normally be called an amended location.

Tannenbaum felt he had been cheated out of the success of the Azure Mining Company, and his partnership with Hidden in the Jarilla Mountains had not produced much turquoise. With the acquisition of the claims on Turquoise Mountain in Courtland, he had achieved the position in the turquoise market he had long sought. Production began immediately, with Rascom as superintendent. He sent two brothers, Nathan and Julius Goldsmith, to oversee his interests. The brothers were either the nephews of Tannenbaum's wife Rachel or related in some other manner on her side of the family.

An August 20, 1895 article in the *Tombstone Epitaph* reported regular shipments were being sent to New York and 100 pounds of turquoise was ready and being sorted for shipment. A *Tombstone Epitaph* article dated September 3, 1895 clearly shows the arrangement with Rascom was temporary when it reports the arrival of Julius Goldsmith, "owner" of the claims, with H.F. Hazelwood, who was to replace Rascom. Hazelwood had worked in some capacity at the Azure mine in the Burros and, although the article claimed he was in charge, Felix Vogel was the superintendent at that time. The report also stated that Rascom was resigning his position to "personally look after his own interests."

Tannenbaum continued to work this property for several years. By 1898 he had turned his attention to other opportunities in California. It is not clear that his claims were not producing or if he simply saw more opportunity elsewhere, but most of his claims were allowed to lapse at some point and fade from the records.

By all accounts, Nick Rascom was a quiet unassuming man. He was born in Illinois sometime around 1850 and had come to the Southwest around 1875, settling in the Gleeson-Courtland area in 1878 or 1879. He was a prolific prospector and located more turquoise mines during The Great American Turquoise Rush than anyone else. By 1895, he had located many claims on Turquoise Mountain that presumably he was mining. He acquired more in 1901. At some point, the core claims of the Azure Mining Company that Kahn and Rothschild held were either allowed to lapse or were transferred. On December 17, 1901, William Cowan, Nelson W. Stevenson, Alfred Stevenson, and William Stevenson deeded to N.C. Rascom the Virginia, Julian, Persian, Jewel, Azure, Nightingale, Turquoise, Asia, Cerulean, Carrie, Lillian, Gem, and the Avalon Mill site for $500. It is curious that the purchase price was so low for this group of claims. On January 3, 1903, Rascom entered into a transaction with Thomas S. Parker and Catherine J. Parker to buy the Avalon, Azure, Asia, Nightingale, Cerulean, Turquoise, Virginia, Cortez, Georgia, Alabama, Santa Ana, and the Carrie under the following arrangement: $2,500 at escrow, $1,500 payable on May 1, 1903, $6,000 payable on January 1, 1904, and 25,000 shares in any company organized by George S. Good. What a curious deed.

First, none of the claims Tannenbaum worked are included, but those that Kahn and Rothschild held are. Second is the entrance of Tom Parker to Courtland. In Chapter 3, we noted Parker's efforts to establish a turquoise cartel in the Burros to compete with the Azure Mining Company. He was not successful in those efforts, and by 1903 had turned his attention to Courtland. We do not know what business arrangement Parker had with Good, but Rascom deeded to Good all of the claims in the Parker deed for $1, which leads to the presumption that all of the payments were made and Rascom ended up with $10,000 and possibly a significant equity interest in Good's business. Considering the cash payment would be worth almost $300,000 today, Rascom did very well. No further evidence of Thomas Parker in the Courtland area exists, but this is not surprising. Although success eluded him in his turquoise aspirations, he accumulated several copper claims that he sold to Phelps Dodge in 1909 for $2MM. He spent the rest of his life in leisure and as a philanthropist helping to fund a hospital in Tyrone, the Phelps Dodge community Mabel Dodge had developed.

Good continued as the principal turquoise operator at Courtland for several years until the end of The Great American Turquoise Rush. One of the last records we found of Rascom was a deed dated July 3, 1906 of the Jewel to L.D. Shattuck. Shattuck went on to be the principal miner in the subsequent turquoise era. Rascom died suddenly in Gleeson on May 1, 1909. He was presumed to be about 60 years old.

Courtland turquoise. Private collection.
Photo courtesy Michael Gomez and Teena Lee Ryan.

Notes

1. R. Sassen, "The Mines and Minerals of Cochise County Arizona," *Lapidary Journal,* July 1972, 670.
2. W.P. Blake, "New Locality of Chalchuite," *American Journal of Science,* vol. 25, 1883, 197.
3. Smith, H. M., "Turquoise," *Arizona Highways,* March 1939, 27.
4. M.I. Jacobson, "Lippman Tannenbaum, President of the Himalaya Mining Company and a Difficult Person," *Mineral News,* September 1910, 5.
5. *The St. John's Herald,* February 9, 1893, vol.9, no. 7.

6

Mineral Park

The town of Mineral Park was founded in 1871 near another mining camp, the town of Chloride, which was the seat of Mohave County at the time, a position Mineral Park assumed in 1877. In 1882, while surveying the route for the Atlantic and Pacific Railroad, which followed the route charted by Beal and the camel corps in 1857, Lewis Kingman put his name on the settlement about 15 miles southeast of Mineral Park. By 1887, Kingman had grown to become the county seat. Between 1875 and 1885, Mineral Park was a thriving community with restaurants, hotels, and a newspaper, the *Mineral Park Miner*. As commerce shifted to Kingman, the town waned and the post office closed in 1912. Today it is a ghost town with only a few remains of the old town.

James W. Haas was born in New York State around 1846 and, as a young man, headed west, working as a miner in Colorado, Wyoming, and Idaho before settling in Mineral Park in the 1870s. His obituary from the *Mohave County Miner* of February 2, 1916 offers an unexpected viewpoint of the man:

"Haas was a most peculiar man, having that peculiar faculty of getting into trouble with his neighbors and those who should be his best friends". It goes on to add, "But that phase is over and his spirit stands before the Almighty Judge of all mankind who will judge all his acts wisely and justly."

James W. Haas is generally credited with the modern day discovery of the Mineral Park turquoise deposits in Mohave County, Arizona, sometime between the mid-1870s and early 1880s. Haas, in an article in *Mining and Scientific Press* published in 1902[1], claimed he made the discovery "about twenty-eight years ago" where Sterrett in the 1906 MRUS says it was in 1885.[2]

Kunz first reported the discovery in 1885, stating that Mr. Bernard Moses brought samples of finely colored turquoise to New York from Mineral Park. He also reported that the areas where the specimens were "show evidence of having been worked by the Indians and Spaniards and a large number of stone hammers were found."[3]

As Haas told his story, while prospecting for precious metals a mile and a half southeast of Mineral Park in an area called Aztec Mountain (aka Turquoise Mountain), he came upon some old mines that had been worked by soldiers from nearby Fort Mohave. Scattered over the ground and dumps were pieces of blue and green stones and ancient stone hammers. He crushed some of the stone and took it to an assayer at the Mineral Park mill, but the results were negative. He sunk the shaft deeper, and after finding nothing new, he abandoned it. Sometime later, upon hearing news that turquoise had been found in that area, he went to investigate and found some men from New Mexico working in the very shaft he had abandoned. They had legally located the claim, but after working it only a short time they left it and never returned.[4]

Later when the claim became available for relocation because of failure to make the annual assessment filing, Haas re-acquired the mine and sent samples of the turquoise to Tiffany's in New York. Chief Gemologist Kunz stated the material was "all right" but would be better at greater depth. Haas dug deeper and when the quality failed to improve, he quit working the claim but did not abandon it. While prospecting farther east on the mountain, he found more prehistoric workings and pieces of blue stone scattered over a large area. He selected samples and sent them to France, Germany, Switzerland, England, and Belgium. Each reply stated they had found some fault with the material, complaining it was too light, too dark, too green, or "too something,"[5] but each also said they would buy three or four pounds and even pay for postage. With no one interested in contributing to development of the mine, Haas allowed the claims to lapse.

In 1887, Sarah Althea Hill-Terry and G.W. Bowers located the Emerald, Blue Gem, and Crown Jewel claims on the southern slopes of Turquoise Mountain[6], but never worked them and allowed the claims to lapse. Although it was then re-located in the name of a Denver Colorado syndicate, only $50 of assessment work was made and the claims again lapsed and laid idle for two more years.

Haas then located the claim yet again and began work. According to Haas: "I sent stone to parties north, south, east and west to advertise it. No one wanted it."[7] This ambivalence to the turquoise from Mineral Park may be attributed to several factors. First, the ATC was experiencing extreme financial difficulties and had declared bankruptcy in 1897 and was in the process of reorganization at the time. The other major turquoise company, the Azure Mining Company, continued to produce high-grade turquoise from the Azure mine and had ample supply. Perhaps the most difficult hurdle for the turquoise from Mineral Park was that it contained much matrix that was not in favor at that time. Yet the prospects for turquoise mining in Mineral Park soon took a dramatic turn.

Aztec (Turquoise) Mountain rough. Turquoise from the old Mineral Park district is today commonly referred to as Kingman, although distinction has been made for both Ithaca Peak and Turquoise Mountain. Though the area is known for its distinctive matrix, this rough demonstrates the type of turquoise miners would have wanted during The Great American Turquoise Rush.

Haas to Doty

In 1897 the ATC filed for bankruptcy. Joseph Doty had served since its inception as an officer of the company and was the sole agent. He was responsible for selling the output of the mines and worked closely with the superintendent, James Patrick McNulty. In spite of their tireless efforts, they were not able to mine sufficient material meeting the strict requirements for non-matrix, sky blue turquoise. Following the bankruptcy, Robert Parker, an associate of one of the principal bondholders, James Stillman, took over management of the mines even though he had no mining or jewelry experience. He demanded Doty increase production and deliver high-grade turquoise or leave.

Doty continued to meet the requirements of Parker and the bondholders, but it was a losing proposition. There was just not enough turquoise of the quality needed. In May of 1899, Doty wrote to McNulty saying prospective new buyers would be examining the mine and he had an offer on the table for the mines himself.[8] The bondholders then changed their minds and decided not to sell the company, remove Doty, and take control of his shares. By late 1899, McNulty received a message from Parker informing him, "Doty is now out of our service," and to notify him if Doty was seen in the area because he believed Doty owed $10,000 to the old company.[9] Most likely the opposite was true. The bondholders put Parker in full control of the management of the mine and as agent of the reorganized ATC. He had no experience in either. One of his first actions as agent was to give Tiffany and Co. exclusive rights to purchase all turquoise found. Doty's attempt to purchase the claims of the ATC had failed and he had been thrown out.

There are two versions of how Haas and Doty came together. The first was that of J.W. Haas himself. A man who had heard about the turquoise went to see Haas while traveling through the area of the Atlantic and Pacific railroad. Under a bond and lease for $10,000, he took some samples to New York. It appears the term bond is used as some form of option or commitment to purchase rather than a debt instrument or form of surety insurance. According to Haas:

> I thought $10,000 would be better to me alive, than $50,000 after I was dead. He got a rich man there interested in it, who put up $2000 cash—$1,000 the promoter was to pay me on the lease and bond and $1,000 for his expenses going and coming from New York. The schemer came out here, gave me $500 and kept the $1,500 and went God knows where—and he is there yet.[10]

Although Haas only named him as "a rich man," the name Joseph G. Doty was on the signed lease and bond. After a couple of months, Haas wrote to Doty alerting him to the facts, which came as a surprise to Doty, and sent an "expert" to settle the business.

John L. Riggs, Haas's stepson, had a slightly different account because he was not aware of the contract details, but the result was the same: Doty controlled the mine on Turquoise Hill with Haas working it for him, though according to Riggs, "this mine never did produce good stone."

The story shifted a mile north of Turquoise Mountain to Ithaca Peak. An old Walapai Indian showed some samples to Charles Sherman, a local prospector and rival of James Haas. According to Riggs, the two men were bitter enemies and once had a gunfight with shotguns and both were wounded. Sherman made several locations of claims all over Ithaca Peak. At that time, Haas was dealing with Doty for the Turquoise Mountain claim. When Doty returned to Mineral Park, Sherman approached him with about five pounds of turquoise that Doty bought for $500. According to Riggs, "They then began to dicker between them for the ground. They spent a very special social evening together, drank from a long bottle quite often and the dickering just like a horse trade proceeded."[11] By morning they had reached an agreement for a purchase price of $9,000 for the claims on the western side of Ithaca Peak, with Sherman keeping those on the east. Riggs continued his story:

Next morning Doty taking Haas along as his expert, went with Sherman onto the ground. Ithaca is a bluff, precipitous, rugged Mountain. Doty balked at the base of the bluffs and sent Haas on with Sherman to look at the mines and determine the boundaries. On their return nothing was said until Sherman dropped out in town. Then Haas told Doty to buy the ground by all means. After some more dickering Sherman agreed if he would give him one thousand down he would wait until he could get the balance forwarded from New York. So Doty borrowed a thousand from Mrs. Haas and the deal was culminated and the great Aztec Turquoise Company of Johns Street New York City came into existence from which millions of profit was made.[12]

Mineral Park, Ithaca Peak and Aztec (Turquoise) Mountain. D.B. Sterrett, *U.S. Geological Survey.* 119.

Ithaca Peak. Aztec Turquoise Company claims. D.B. Sterrett, *U.S. Geological Survey.* 120.

Ithaca Peak. Southwest Turquoise Company, Arizona Turquoise Company, Los Angeles Gem Company, and other claims. D.B. Sterrett, *U.S. Geological Survey*, 121.

Mr. Joseph G. Doty of New York and James W. Hass of Mineral Park, Mohave County Arizona. Scene from Turquoise Mountain, June 1, 1901, Mohave Museum of History and Arts.

Haas and Doty at camp June 1, 1901. The Aztec Turquoise Company. Mohave Museum of History and Arts.

The Aztec Turquoise Company

The Aztec Turquoise Company was incorporated on June 29, 1900 with offices in New York City. The shareholders—John Elsey, Jersey City, New Jersey; Joseph G. Doty, Wyoming, New Jersey; Henry L. Warnstedt, New York City; Charles N. Laidlaw Jr., New York City, and Edward R. Grant, Bayonne, New Jersey—each subscribed for $2,000 with $200 paid for 400 shares. Under the supervision of Haas, the company soon began shipping turquoise. As reported in the *Mohave County Miner,* by October Doty was shipping 25 pounds a week.[13]

In Cerrillos, the financial problems of the ATC continued and they were forced to make many cost cuts. In November, Ed McNulty, James P. McNulty's son and an important member of the production team, quit and went to work for his father-in-law in Prescott, Arizona. By July 1902, Doty was in Cerrillos looking for workers for the Aztec operations. McNulty senior wrote to his son, and Ed accepted the offer and went to work for Doty as superintendent of the Aztec mining operations, taking over from Haas who left to work his other claims. By November 1902, McNulty wrote to Parker he had heard the Aztec Company was making large shipments from Kingman, Arizona.[14] According to Sterrett:

> The principal work of the Aztec Company has been on the Monte Cristo (Montie Christie) claim on the southeast end of Ithaca Peak, near the top; the Queen claim on the south side of the west end of Ithaca Peak; the Peacock claim, on the north side of Aztec Mountain; the Aztec and Turquoise King claims, on the south side of Aztec Mountain.[15]

Haas had deeded the claims to Doty on May 22, 1901,[16] and Sherman had done so on July 7, 1901.[17] Doty then deeded all of the claims to the Aztec Mining Company in 1901 and 1902,[18] and work began immediately. A report from the *Mining and Scientific Press* of December 1901 states that a holding cistern of 800 barrels in capacity had been dug out of the rock to hold rain and snow melt to provide water for the mining work. In addition, 22 men were working under the direction of James Haas and over $27,000 had been spent on development and equipment.

Turquoise camp, Ithaca Peak. Courtesy Mohave County Museum of History and Arts.

Ithaca Peak looking east towards the Aztec claim of the Aztec Turquoise Company. *Mining and Scientific Press*, ca. 1908.

Competition

A central theme of The Great American Turquoise Rush was the competition of the companies operating in different areas for dominance in the market. Doty, as agent for the ATC, had competed with the rival Azure Mining Company located in the Burros. Now he was part of the Aztec Turquoise Company, competing with his former company and their main competitor. Others soon entered the market in Mineral Park.

According to Riggs, when bitter rivals Haas and Sherman walked the claims on Ithaca Peak, upon returning to town Haas recommended the purchase of the claims on the west side of the mountain but not the east, which he condemned as inferior. Riggs claimed this was done out of spite to keep Sherman from benefitting from the additional sale. Sherman then entered into negotiations for the remaining claims. Riggs presented a colorful account:

> Some promoters came along and after much chin music they got Sherman to join them in a gem company to cut and market the stone, got him tied into an agreement so they personally owned half of the ground. When Sherman found they could not do the proper financing to get going, or

he could not get away from it, finally came to an agreement to segregate the ground. Sherman drew a line through the center and gave them their choice. They took the south side and from that ground sprang the Southwest Turquoise Company of Los Angeles.[19]

The Southwest Turquoise Company was incorporated in 1903. An article from the *Los Angeles Herald* of May 24, 1903 reported:

As an indication of the diverse nature of the mineral deposits in Mohave County W.J. Tarr of Los Angeles and R.A. McMullen of West Superior, Wisconsin, have purchased the interest of John B. Davis, S.G. McKesson and E.F. Thompson in turquoise properties at Mineral Park. In company with Charles E. Sherman of Mineral Park, the owner of other valuable turquoise interests there, they have taken steps to incorporate as the Southwest Turquoise Company with a capital stock of $500,000. Mr. Sherman will manage the mines, Mr. Tarr will manage the shops and office in Los Angeles while Mr. McMullen will be special trade agent.[20]

The principal area of production for the company was the Ithaca claim.[21] Sherman still retained one and a half claims on the east side of Ithaca Peak that he later sold to Edward E. Peck and George Burkhardt of Los Angeles for $5,000. This must have been around 1904 because Peck had moved to Los Angeles about that time, following a series of bad investments in Michigan. He worked as a lapidary for the California Gem Company, saved some money, formed Peck and Burkhardt, and purchased the turquoise claims. They split the property and sold the best half to a Frank L. McCracken and George Bell, both from Denver, for $6,000. Peck and Burkhardt formed the Los Angeles Gem Company, with offices in Los Angeles. Peck bought out Burkhardt in 1908 and purchased gem claims in Nevada the same year, including several variscite claims in the Candelaria Hills. In 1910, he formed the International Mines Company, which owned valuable gold and silver properties.

Bell and McCracken formed the Arizona Turquoise Company, incorporated in 1908. The principal claim was the William Tell. The company had offices in Denver, where Bell had long operated his lapidary business, and sold the turquoise in New York. Although others were mining in the area, including the Mineral Park Turquoise Company operating two claims, and James Uncapher, John Caswell, and John Kay who each worked one claim, these four companies—the Aztec Turquoise Company, the Southwest Turquoise Company, the Los Angeles Gem Company, and the Arizona Turquoise Company—were the principal competitors.

East side of Ithaca Peak, looking northwest from above Southwest Turquoise Company mine. Arizona Turquoise Company mine is on left and Los Angeles Gem Company mine is on the right. D.B. Sterrett, *U.S. Geological Survey*, 124.

Ithaca Peak, looking north towards Mineral Park Turquoise Company mine. D.B. Sterrett, *U.S. Geological Survey*, 125.

Companies headquartered in New York City, selling to east coast and European markets, dominated The Great American Turquoise Rush. The jewelry created with this turquoise was designed in the same Victorian style that had been in fashion for decades and reflected established ideas about fashion and its role in society and the greater social culture. The turn of the century introduced dramatic changes in the areas of science, art, and politics. The old customs were giving way to the new in often dramatic ways. In 1905, a Swiss patent clerk published a somewhat obscure scientific paper, *The Special Theory of Relativity*, which altered the way people thought the world worked. In 1907, Picasso unveiled Les Desmoilles D'Avignon and turned the art world upside down. The political atmosphere of the first decade was tumultuous across the globe. Radical anarchists sought to overturn what they considered centuries of oppression, and more moderate voices spoke of limiting the power of unrestricted market capitalism. President Theodore Roosevelt actively campaigned against the large corporate trusts that dominated American commerce, using the Sherman Antitrust Act as his primary weapon.

Fashion trends reflected the greater changes affecting society. Under the guidance of Louis Comfort Tiffany, Tiffany and Co. set upon a path for which it is still known. Influenced by William Morris, Tiffany created pottery in this style from 1880–1910. His glass designs defined the company's style and led the way to Art Deco. In the field of jewelry design, George Paulding Farnham created bold new designs. Tiffany and Co.'s brand had been developed during the nineteenth century on an image of dependable quality and service, symbolized by the Tiffany Blue Box. Although the company retained that legacy, in the new century they developed a brand that connoted elegance and design innovation. It was indeed a brave new world.

Some have speculated the end of The Great American Turquoise Rush was brought on by the introduction of matrix in the turquoise. The presence of matrix was certainly a major factor in limiting production because buyers favored only the clear blue stone. This was a factor in the ATC's financial difficulties because they could not produce enough of the quality of turquoise the New York buyers required, but it was not the principal cause of the collapse in turquoise prices at the end of the first decade of the new century. The confluence of the financial crisis of 1907, which caused the recession of 1908, and the change in jewelry fashion trends were the major causes. A contributing factor was the presence of copper in many of the areas that contained turquoise. The economic benefit of extracting copper was more attractive than that for turquoise. John Riggs summed this up when describing the copper ore all around the turquoise mines at Mineral Park: "Hence the principal detriment to the Turquoise, too much copper."

Mineral Park was important to the story of The Great American Turquoise Rush for two primary reasons. First, this was the first time ownership and marketing efforts began to move from the East Coast to the West. The Southwest Turquoise Company main office was in Los Angeles. The Los Angeles Gem Company operated only in the West, and expanded their operation into other gem mines in Nevada. For the first time, matrix turquoise was marketed as special in its own right and even superior to the clear blue that had been the standard. The clear blue was difficult to find in larger pieces, requiring the cabochons to be cut small and set with other small gemstones. Matrix turquoise allowed the creation of very different designs with larger stones.

The motto of the Southwest Turquoise Company was "Our own mines, our own shops, our own prices." This sentiment was one shared by the other companies competing for dominance in the market, although not stated so openly. The company's 1908 catalog described turquoise:

> It occurs in various shades of blue and green. The most valued color among Western races are the rich sky blue but among many of the Eastern people the more abundant green shades are preferred. The matrix turquoise is the most popular on account of the beautiful marking. The stones are like beautiful dream pictures and no two are alike. The "cobweb turquoise" surpasses all other in its beautiful markings. This is very rare as there is only one mine which has this particular quality.

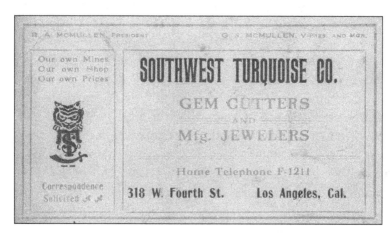

Southwest Turquoise Company card.

Postcard of Southwest Turquoise Company (front), 1906.

Postcard of Southwest Turquoise Company (back), 1906.
The Balloon Route Excursion was a tour of Los Angeles by trolley car.
The balloon was a reference to the shape of the tour route.

Southwest Turquoise Company showroom.

The Southwest Turquoise Company was clearly marketing to a developing tourist market. This is demonstrated in their *List of Specimens* booklet from about 1908 where they encouraged the purchase of a souvenir turquoise nugget:

> A Valuable Souvenir. This is not the year of '49 but one quite as important to many a traveler. You have come here to enjoy our wonderful climate and the many interesting things that have been developed since that time. Knowing how much you would enjoy returning home the proud possessor of a nugget from the Far West, we have contemplated your wish and have prepared a nugget of turquoise which comes from our mines, located directly on the road that was traveled by these same nugget hunters. The price is fifty cents. This makes one of the best and most interesting souvenirs of the West.

George Bell was a lapidary from Denver. He had been involved with turquoise mining in Jarilla, New Mexico and was a well know cutter. The *Arizona Republican* reported: "George Bell lapidary is cutting for Dr. George Hamilton of La Jara, a matrix turquoise weighing 1500 carats newly discovered one and one half miles west of the Rio Grande near New Mexico."[22] In the Arizona Turquoise Company's 1908 catalog is an explanation of how the company works their remote and unique turquoise mine in Mohave County where turquoise runs in veins of matrix they named "Mother Rock":

Instead of grinding away the matrix and using only the small Pure Turquoise remaining *we cut and polish Matrix and Turquoise together.* (Italics theirs). This produces a fine large Turquoise Matrix from the same rough piece that we would otherwise be able to cut but one small one-color Turquoise, so that these beautifully marked large stones cost no more than much smaller Pure stones. The Matrix takes an equally high polish with the Turquoise, and its varying brown shading with the rich blue of the Turquoise, forms one of those beautiful harmonies of Nature of which the eye never tires.

We see in the following photo a display of turquoise cabochons that is familiar to anyone buying turquoise today. This is an early example of the trend that increased as tourism developed in the Southwest. Along with the expansion of the railroads came support services travelers required. Fred Harvey started his company providing meals at railroad stations, and then expanded into hotels. With the rise of tourism, demand grew for souvenirs, or curios, to which the Harvey organization and others responded with Indian-style jewelry, some handmade by American Indians and some mass-produced by Mexican workers. In the twentieth century, the story of turquoise will be closely tied to the evolution of American Indian jewelry from curio, to craft, to fine art.

Arizona Turquoise Company 1908 advertisement.

The efforts of these companies to expand the market for turquoise jewelry was too little too late when they were confronted in 1910 with the collapse of the turquoise market. As prices dropped, economic feasibility disappeared and mine production ceased. Joseph Doty died in 1907. The corporate entity of the Aztec Turquoise Company was dissolved on September 24, 1910. In Chapter 8 we will see how the changing trends presented here continued and how turquoise was transformed.

The lasting legacy of early turquoise mining at Mineral Peak was the beautiful turquoise the world knows as Kingman. All of the turquoise from Ithaca Peak, Turquoise Mountain, and Kingman comes from the area of Mineral Park first mined during The Great American Turquoise Rush and continues to be mined today.

Ithaca Peak turquoise. Private collection.
Photo courtesy Michael Gomez and Teena Lee Ryan.

**Kingman black web turquoise (cobweb). Private collection.
Photo courtesy Michael Gomez and Teena Lee Ryan.**

Notes

1. J.W. Haas, *Mining and Scientific Press*, 08/23/1902, 102.
2. D.B. Sterrett, *Mining Resources of the United States, 1906*, 1234.
3. G.F. Kunz, *Mineral Resources of the United States, 1883–1884*, 767.
4. Haas, 103.
5. Ibid.
6. Mohave County Recorder Book K, 137–139.
7. Haas, 103.
8. McCraw, *Tiffany Blue*, 32.
9. Ibid., 47–48.
10. Haas, 103.
11. J.L. Riggs, *Manuscripts of John L. Riggs, 1924–1925*, Arizona Historical Society.
12. Ibid.
13. *Mohave County Miner*, October 6, 1900.
14. McCraw, *Tiffany Blue*, 120.
15. D.B. Sterrett, *Mineral Resources of the United States, 1909*, 848.
16. Mohave County Recorder Book 15, 48.
17. Mohave County Recorder Book 14, 258.
18. Ibid., 289–294, 607.
19. J.L. Riggs, *Manuscripts of John L. Riggs, 1924–1925*, Arizona Historical Society.
20. *Los Angeles Herald*, May 24, 1903, 7.
21. D.B. Sterrett, *Mineral Resources of the United States, 1909*, 851.
22. *The Arizona Republican*, July 29, 1901, 2.

California, Nevada, and Colorado

7

Crescent Peak, Halloran Springs, and the Royal Blue

Discovery at Crescent Peak and the Toltec Gem Mining Company

The Crescent mining district lies about seventeen miles west of Searchlight, Nevada, which itself is about 60 miles northwest of Kingman, Arizona and the claims at Mineral Park. Halloran Springs is about 40 miles west of Crescent Peak, about 15 miles northeast of Baker, California in the Mohave desert along old Route 91, now Interstate 15, running between Los Angeles and Las Vegas. The Royal Blue mine, located in the Tonopah mining district, is about 300 miles northwest of Crescent Peak.

In 1896, George Simmons was prospecting in the Crescent mining district of Lincoln County, Nevada when he came across a piece of stained quartz. Often this would indicate the presence of copper, but Simmons had seen similar material when he was in the Burro Mountains of New Mexico years earlier and recognized it might be turquoise. He searched for eight months before locating a mine that had been worked long ago. As with other examples of prehistoric mining efforts, the prospectors, who generally held American Indians in low regard, believed this must have been the effort of a much more developed society.

Morrissey reported that Simmons believed the presence of stone tools and a lapidary shop indicated these miners were part of an economy that was involved in the transport of finished stone rather than rough ore, and that the Indians of his day or their forebears were not capable of such work and attributed the effort to the ancient Toltec and Aztecs. Only more recently have we learned of the sophisticated mining and trade routes of the Ancestral Puebloan throughout the southwest.[1]

Simmons sent some of the samples from this mine to a lapidary in Denver, William Kley, who not only cut some stones but also put Simmons in touch with another German lapidary, William Petry, who Simmons hired to set up a lapidary shop at the mine. Simmons took the cut stones to New York and even London but could not find the financial backers he needed to develop the claim. In late 1897 or 1898, he found investors. Charles F. Wood and Company was a dealer in cut diamonds operating from offices on 1 Maiden Lane in New York City in partnership with his brothers, John B. Wood and Elmer Wood. Along with another investor, John Lamont, a lapidary, and Simmons, they formed the Toltec Gem Mining Company and began working the mine. It is interesting to note that the *Salt Lake Herald* reports, regarding their turquoise holdings, that they could "limit or increase the supply at their will and they can fix the price as effectively for turquoise as can the DeBeers company of South Africa for diamonds."[2] This would indicate the intention of New York firms to create a pricing cartel—which we noted in both Cerrillos and the Burros—and was continuing with efforts in Nevada and, as we shall soon see, in California.

Questions surround the identity of the Wood family, who had the Toltec Gem Mining Company. Some have identified them as J.R. Wood and Sons, prominent wholesale jewelers with a large production facility in Brooklyn, New York. This John R. Wood had first started in the jewelry business in 1850, and his sons Rawson, St. John, and Harry joined him. We do not know if the different families of Wood were related but we can be sure the owners of the Toltec were those operating Charles F. Wood and Company.[3] The families were also certainly familiar with each other as J.R. Wood had offices at 21 Maiden Lane and Charles F. Wood had offices at 14 Maiden Lane, which were moved to 1 Maiden Lane in 1898.[4] The Trow Corporation Directory of 1908 lists for the Toltec Gem Mining Company: Charles F. Wood, President; John B. Wood, Secretary; with capital of $500,000; Directors Charles F., John B., and Elmer E. Wood; and John Lamont. George Simmons, as we shall soon learn, was no longer involved with the company at that time. Simmons, in addition to being an original shareholder in the Toltec, served as manager of the turquoise operations at Crescent Peak, with William Petry overseeing the cutting and William Miller acting as foreman of the miners.

Crescent Peak Mine of the Toltec Gem Mining Company August 1913. Sterrett incorrectly identified this series of photos as the J.R. Wood turquoise mine rather than J.B. Wood. D.B. Sterrett, *U.S. Geological Survey*, 567.

Workings in the gulch of Crescent Peak Mine shown in photo 77. D.B. Sterrett, *U.S. Geological Survey*, 568.

Crescent Peak Mine across gulch towards workings on south side of turquoise area with open cut and two tunnels. The ancient works are seen around the low rocky knob on right. August 1913. D.B. Sterrett, *U.S. Geological Survey*, 569.

Crescent Peak turquoise. The Crescent Peak Mine, also known as the Simmons Mine, is located in Clark County, Nevada. The patent was issued June 15,1908 for eleven claims on 220.28 acres making this the largest group of turquoise patent claims ever issued in the United States and this does not include other patent claims issued to the company in California. The mine is located primarily on two claims, the Aztec and the Right Blue. Originally part of Lincoln County, Clark County was separated in 1908. This turquoise is often incorrectly referred to as Searchlight. Photo by Robert Stapp.

Halloran Springs turquoise. Riffian Blue Mine, old Middle Camp. Photo by Robert Stapp.

Conflicting reports exist of the early development of turquoise mining at Halloran Springs. George Kunz first announced the discovery in the 1897 *MRUS*. He stated that near Manvel, Mr. T.C. Basset noticed some float rock stained with blue. Digging down he found a vein of turquoise at a depth of about 20 feet, showing high-grade color. As had been the case in all the other turquoise discoveries in our narrative, stone hammers were discovered, indicating prehistoric mining.[5] This led to the location being named the Stone Hammer mine. According to Vredenburgh in the *History of Mining in the Halloran Hills, Shadow Mountains, and Silurian Hills*, the Gem was located in the vicinity of the old digs on May 20, 1896, and three more claims located nearby on August 9, 1896.[6] Malcom J. Rogers, in his 1929 archeological report of the area for the San Diego Museum, reported that, "Mr. James Hyten, of Baker, informs me that his brother, William Hyten, now deceased, discovered these mines about 38 years ago, but that he was the first to file claim to them in 1895."[7] Sterrett proposes an even different story:

According to the information furnished by Mr. Gus Hamstadt, of Nipton, the turquoise deposits were discovered by an Indian named Prospector Johnnie, who located them in 1894 in partnership with G. Washington and Peter Phifer. Mr. Hamstadt carried some of the turquoise to New York in 1896, selling a quantity and getting parties interested in the deposits.

Sterrett misidentified the two Wood companies and this confusion continued, no doubt due to the high regard many hold for him.

Nazelrod noted turquoise that consisted of turquoise pseudomorphs in granite found near the Chowchillas River was first discovered in California in 1864 by J.D. Whitney in Fresno County. He offered no corroborative evidence to this claim. He also stated that the next discovery was made in 1879 by T.C. Basset, most likely at what would be known as East Camp. He also reported that William Hyten discovered the buried Indian mines at West Camp in 1898, upon which time he located six claims and sold them to the Himalaya Mining Company, and then remained as superintendent. The company mined the area until the turquoise played out then moved their operations to Nevada's Royston District.[8] It is possible Hyten located the claims in West Camp purchased by the Himalaya Mining Company and patented in 1903. Nazelrod's reports must be regarded as anecdotal because they are not substantiated by supporting evidence. Murdoch and Webb showed the Stone Hammer Mine in Middle Camp and the Toltec Mine in East Camp (see map). The patent claims issued to J.B. Wood of the Toltec Gem Mining Company in 1904 show that, although the Stone Hammer was in Middle Camp, the Toltec was in West Camp. Rogers stated, with regard to the old mines:

> Although many of these mines have been obliterated by modern work, especially at the Toltec group (East Camp) it is possible to identify with certainty fifty aboriginal workings at the Himalaya group (West Camp), twenty at the Middle group, and for the Toltec group I take Mr. Hyten's estimate of two hundred, this count having been made prior to modern disfiguration.[9]

It is unclear when operations began in the area, although an April 1898 notice in *Mining and Scientific Press* referenced turquoise being shipped to Amsterdam, including a piece weighing 210 carats. We know that by March 1898, word of the discovery had reached the newspaper, *The San Francisco Call*, which financed an exploration of the old mine led by Dr. Gustav Eisen, an archeologist at the California Academy of Sciences. In three lengthy articles on March 18, 19, and 27, the paper detailed the expedition. Of particular interest were the comments of Dr. Eisen who, for perhaps the first time, identified the aboriginal miners that inhabited the Southwest as being a distinct group from either the Toltec or Aztec of Mexico:

> It is safe to say that the discovery of prehistoric turquoise mines of California and certain traces of the prehistoric race of Indians which worked those mines and traded with the wealth extracted from them forms the most important discovery yet made in the history of the native races of the Pacific Coast. It brings us to close contact with a race of Indian vastly superior to those now existing on this coast, immensely more civilized than any of which we so far have had any knowledge, with the exception of the Aztecs and the Mayas of Mexico and Central America.

Eisen described the discovery of five groups of relics, including high-quality turquoise stones, thousands of detailed hieroglyphs, many stone implements, and an extensive cave network that might have served as shelter for the miners.[10] Other local authorities supported Eisen's conclusion, including a Professor Le Conte from a "local" university who stated, "Undoubtedly the people who worked the mines and graved the strange characters on the walls of the rock are the same tribe that constructed extensive irrigation works and built rude cities through the cliff regions of Arizona."[11]

This opinion was supported in the Rogers report of 1929 in which he said that evidence indicated the mines to be the work of Puebloan people or an earlier group.[12] Leonard and Drover (1980) determined through carbon dating that there had been three distinct phases of mining activity, with the earliest occurring between A.D. 400 and A.D. 700, followed by a second of A.D. 1090–1120, and the third phase of A.D. 1200–1900.[13]

On less sound science is the anecdotal tale Eisen recounts from a local native known as Indian Johnny, who had heard the tale from his father who had heard the same from his: A thousand years ago the area was inhabited by the Desert Mohaves. There came from the South or West a tribe of Indians searching for precious gems. They were very different from the Desert Mohaves, with fairer skin and hair. They were more civilized and knew how to work the mines and made writing on the cliffs. They were peaceful and lived in peace with the Desert Mohaves. The Paiutes, another tribe in the area and the tribe of Indian Johnny, did not like that the Desert Mohaves were learning new things and thought the newcomers were crazy for marking writing on the cliffs, so they made war on both the foreign Indians and the Desert Mohaves, killing most of them.

The reports in the *Call* created great interest in the area. Sometime after October 1898, the newly formed Toltec Gem Mining Company, which had just begun operations in Crescent Peak, Nevada 40 miles to the east, began work on 3 groups of claims on or near Turquoise Mountain, which became known as East Camp, Middle Camp, and West Camp. A well was sunk at East Camp along with structures to house the miners. Production soon began, with turquoise estimated at a value in 1900 between $20,000 and $28,000 (between $500,000 and $700,000 in current dollars) shipped to New York.

Mining records give a different picture about the location and development of the area. In researching the San Bernardino County mining records, Bill Jones found the following locations by P.R. Washington: 2/17/1897 the Lost Mining claim, 02/26/1897 the Legal Tender claim, 02/27/1897 the Chief claim, 04/27/1897 the Pienroum, 09/21/1897 the Barney Blue claim. On 09/21/1897, Washington located the additional claims with Thomas Kennedy: the Jesuit, Occidental, Madre, Heroic Girl, Romantic Boy, and the Red and Blue Gem. On 10/05/1897 the Toltec, and 10/19/1897 Kennedy and Washington located the Stone Hammer claims. Two months later, on 12/16/1897, an annual assessment notice for the year 1897 was filed for the Barney Blue, Montezuma, Aztec, Toltec, Blue Gem, Heroic Girl, Stone Hammer, Madre, Padre, Occidental, Jesuit, Gem, Jewell, Turquois, and Ancient Mines. The names listed on the filing were P.R. Washinton, Peter Pfeiffer, Thomas Kennedy, and J.W. Stine, indicating these prospectors were responsible for the early locations of the claims in the district. Whatever earlier claims may have been located, these are the ones on record as of this date.

Although it appears the Toltec Gem Mining Company was active in 1899, the next we find in the records is an annual assessment filing for the year 1900 filed on 01/31/1901 by Milton Mundy for J.B. Wood for the Lost Mining, Chief, Occidental, Madre, Romantic Boy, Toltec, Stone Hammer, Bright Blue, Tiger, Hill, Scrap, Searchlight, Hattie, Lieutenant Hobson, Jewell, Aztec, Montezuma, Padre, and Ancient Mining claims. This shows that sometime in late 1898 or in 1899, they obtained these claims most likely through lease from the owners. This is indicated by the patent mining claims issued to J.B. Wood for the claims of East Camp, Middle Camp, West Camp, and the Lost Lode mining and mill site claim in 1904 that state Wood purchased the claims as follows:

East Camp, the Valuable, Madre, Padre, and Occidental claims on 12/17/1902; Middle Camp, the Searchlight, Stone Hammer, Chief, Lieutenant Hobson, Bright Blue, Hill, Scrap, Tiger, Romantic Boy, and Hattie claims on 12/26/1902; West Camp, the Montezuma, Aztec, and Toltec claims on 12/17/1902; and the Lost Lode mining and mill site on 12/26/1902.[14] According to this information, the location of the Toltec is in the West Camp rather than the East Camp. It is clear the Toltec Gem Mining Company owned these claims by no later than December of 1902, and had likely been operating on many of them since early 1899.

East Camp turquoise mine of Toltec Gem Mining Company towards the camp and part of the principal workings. D.B. Sterrett, *U.S. Geological Survey*, 573.

East Camp turquoise mine west down canyon from the principal workings with dumps in the foreground. D.B. Sterrett, *U.S. Geological Survey*, 576.

Tannenbaum and the Himalaya Mining Company

During The Great American Turquoise Rush, similarities existed in all of the areas producing turquoise. In each instance, prospectors located the claims. These included Chauncey Story and Michael O'Neil in Cerrillos, Nicolas Rascom in the Burros and Courtland, James Haas and Charles Sherman in Mineral Park, George Simmons at Crescent Peak, and P.R. Washington at Halloran Springs. They sold those claims to investors, mainly from New York City—including Charles L. Tiffany with the ATC; Gyulo Armeny, the Kahn Brothers, and Meyer Rothschild of the Azure Mining Company; and the Wood brothers of the Toltec Gem Mining Company—who developed the mines with the help of local agents like Joseph Doty with the ATC and George Simmons with the Toltec. Production at the mines relied upon talented and dependable superintendents such as J.P. McNulty in Cerrillos and Felix Vogel at the Azure.

The various corporate investors faced challenges and achieved success. Although the turquoise market was competitive, uncertain reserves and on-going economic challenges eroded the companies' financial strength. Only the Azure Mining Company appeared to have remained relatively unscathed through the entire 20 years of The Great American Turquoise Rush, primarily due to the great reserves present in the Elizabeth Pocket that provided them with measurable inventory they could match to the particular demands of the market. Of all the corporate players, none was as committed to achieving success in the turquoise market as Julius Lippman Tannenbaum.

As we have noted, Tannenbaum was a successful jeweler and diamond broker in New York City. He was, by most accounts, generous with his family, friends, and employees but very quick tempered. He was litigious to a high degree and during his entire professional life was frequently involved in a court proceeding either as defendant or plaintiff.

As we saw in Chapter 5, it appears Tannenbaum leveraged his court judgment regarding his dispute with Gyulo Armeny in obtaining turquoise claims in Courtland, worked after 1895. Yet for Tannenbaum, as for the other investors during The Great American Turquoise Rush, for all their interest in building a dominant position in the market, turquoise remained only a relatively small part of their entire business ventures. Total sales of Tiffany and Co. dwarfed the sale of turquoise jewelry. Armeny remained partners in a successful fountain pen company, the Kahn brothers were established diamond importers that with Meyer Rothschild founded the American Gem Company, which became the American Gem and Pearl Company, mining diverse minerals including aquamarine, emeralds, rhodolyte, amazonite, amethyst, and gem beryl. In his book, *Gem Cutting at Gem Cove,* Russell states:

> Clearly, the American Gem and Pearl Company actively sought to augment the humdrum array of commonly available gem materials which glutted most jewelers inventories with more unusual stones. While they did not shy away from imported gem rough, establishing dependable domestic sources could at least partially buffer the company from attempts by competitors to monopolize major foreign gem sources, as Edwin Streeter and Sons attempted to do with the legendary ruby mines of Mogok in Myanmar.[15]

Tannenbaum was no different than his competitors in wanting to offer a diversified product line of various gems. Although the existence of tourmaline in the Mesa Grande area near San Diego had been mentioned in anecdotal reports, it was not until the late 1890s that interest began to increase rapidly.

Gail Lewis is credited with the first discovery of a tourmaline mine at

Mesa Grande in 1898, but by 1899 and 1900, Frank Wright and C. R. (Russell) Orcutt had begun prospecting and sending samples to New York City. These came to the attention of Tannenbaum, who sent his agents Archibald E. Heighway, Jr. and J. Goodman Braye to investigate. They staked claims in the public land that had been improperly located previously. This initiated a legal battle, for which Tannenbaum was no stranger, and was settled by 1904 with the Himalaya Mining Company securing the claims.

The earliest mention of the Himalaya Mining Company we found is in the *Trow Directory of Corporations* of 1901, which lists Lippman Tannenbaum as president, Hugo Oppenheim as secretary, and Benedict B. Lederer as treasurer, with capitalization of $1MM. The directors, who presumably were also shareholders, were, in addition to the officers, Max M. Tannenbaum, Lippman's oldest son, James McCormick, Sigmund Lederer, and Adolph Lederer, with offices located at the same address as L. Tannenbaum and Company, 52 Nassau Street, New York, New York.[16] The market was strong for tourmaline due in large part to demand from China. Supposedly the Ch'ing Dynasty Dowager Empress was impressed when Charles L. Tiffany obtained some of the French crown jewels in 1887, and she ordered a large amount of pink tourmaline from Tiffany and Co. in 1901.

Although having such a large customer increased demand, it also contributed to the collapse of the tourmaline market following the revolution in China in 1911, which forced the close of the tourmaline operations in 1912. Braye, who promoted himself as the "Black Millionaire," served as manager of the tourmaline mining operations for the Himalaya Mining Company. In an age of racism and segregation in many parts of the United States, Braye was a success story. He had been taken in by Tannenbaum as a youth, educated as a geologist at Cornell, and developed a reputation as a gem expert working for Tannenbaum

Although it may have been the prospect of tourmaline that brought Tannenbaum to California, it did not take long for him to recognize the opportunities for turquoise in Halloran Springs. According to Vredenburgh, the Himalaya claim was located in West Camp on August 7, 1899 near the Toltec's claims, and Tannenbaum purchased four additional claims in the area in 1901. Patents were issued for claims to the Himalaya Mining Company on September 28, 1903, and patents issued in the name of J.B. Wood for Middle Camp and Lost Lode mill site on February 18, 1904, East Camp on March 11, 1904, and West Camp on April 1, 1904. Although much turquoise appears to have been shipped, the tourmaline mines were the primary focus of the Himalaya Mining

Company, with no turquoise production noted after 1904 from the West Camp mines.

One other participant in California was the California Gem Company. Offices were at 322 South Spring St. in Los Angeles where they had a retail outlet. They advertised genuine matrix turquoise as well as other gemstones including opals, garnets, and pearls. They operated the Gove mine, which also became known as the California Gem mine. In the 1909 *MRUS* (published in 1911), Sterrett commented in depth about the mine. He stated the mine, operated in 1908 by C.A. Gove, was in the Mohave desert about two miles west of the Cottonwood siding of the Santa Fe Railroad and was in a low ridge that sloped down to the Mohave River. The best turquoise was pure light blue to dark blue. This indicates that although the company advertised matrix, their best turquoise was considered the pure blue non-matrix favored at the time. In the 1972 Rex Arrowsmith reprint of Pogue's *Turquois* (and in subsequent editions), turquoise from the Gove mine is featured on the inside cover.

In his research at the *San Bernardino County Recorder,* Bill Jones found Location Notices dated January 1, 1908 for the True Blue Mine and Red Rover Mine in the name of the California Gem Company, signed by John J. Reed as agent for Mart Mourning. On December 30, 1908 there is a Proof of Labor annual assessment filed by C.A. Gove. By 1909 Sterrett reported the mine as the Gove, so we might imagine the decision was made to identify the claims with the man heading the California Gem Company, for marketing purposes, much in the manner the Muñiz claim in Cerrillos became known as the Tiffany.

Himalaya Mining Company turquoise mine West Camp. The photo is taken from 125 yards west of camp looking north with the trail to the mine in the center. The mine is in the low hills in front of the rocky point to the left of center. D.B. Sterrett, *U.S. Geological Survey, June 1911, 409.*

Looking southeast towards the Himalaya Mining Company turquoise mine West Camp main works, June 1911. D.B. Sterrett, *U.S. Geological Survey*, 411.

Himalaya Mining Company turquoise mine West Camp main works looking across the open cut from bench above the entrance tunnel and showing different tunnels and stopes, June 1911. D.B. Sterrett, 413. *U.S. Geological Survey.*

Gove turquoise mine. D.B. Sterrett, *U.S. Geological Survey*, 175.

J.L. Clayton is generally credited with the discovery of turquoise in Nevada sometime in the mid-1860s, about five miles from the town of Columbus in the Candelaria Hills. Following the discovery of the Comstock silver lode in 1859, prospectors covered the state. Hoffman reported this discovery in 1878 in *Mineralogy of Nevada.*[17] Silliman in 1882,[18] Kunz in 1890,[19] and Pogue in 1915[20] confirmed this discovery. There was no economic incentive to mine the stone at that time because turquoise sold for the price of coal.

In late March 1903, J.L. and U.C. Workman of Tonopah, Nevada located the Royal Blue about eight miles north of Crow Springs on the western slopes of what they referred to as Quartzite Mountain in what is now known as the Royston District. This was followed in early April by their locations of the Snowstorm, Blue Bird, Aztec, and Blue Bell.[21] All were on the eastern slope of the same Quartzite Mountain as the Royal Blue. After about a year, the Workmans sold the Royal Blue to William Petry for $2,500. Petry had worked for George Simmons as a lapidary for the Toltec Gem Mining Company at their Crescent Peak mines. He wasted no time in getting a survey completed to file a patent claim.

On November 14, 1908, Petry sold the Royal Blue as well as the Azure Blue, Corona Turquoise, Oriental Blue, and the Justice Fraction to the Himalaya Mining Company through its representative Lippman Tannenbaum, under agreement for transfer to be completed after installment payments. Although the purchase price is not disclosed, Petry paid $2,500 for the single Royal Blue Claim, leading to speculation the group price could certainly have been in excess of $10,000. Tannenbaum took the title in his own name and on May 24, 1910, he transferred the entire group into the name of the Himalaya Mining Co for consideration of $1. The Royal Blue was worked hard during the years 1908 and 1909 under the supervision of Julius Goldsmith, Tannenbaum's nephew, who had also supervised the turquoise operations in Courtland, Arizona and the Himalaya turquoise mine at West Camp in Halloran Springs. At no small expense, buildings were constructed—a home for Goldsmith and his wife, and a designated cabin for sorting the turquoise. This investment was justified by the Royal Blue's production reports, at times exceeding 1,200 pounds a month. Petry later claimed the Royal Blue produced over $5MM worth of turquoise.[22]

The Royal Blue turquoise mine of the Himalaya Mining Company, Esmeralda County, Nevada, looking east towards the camp and mine. D.B. Sterrett, *U.S. Geological Survey*, 196.

Julius Goldsmith and his wife in front of cabin at the Royal Blue in 1908 or 1909. D.B. Sterrett, *U.S. Geological Survey*, 202.

The Royal Blue mine, looking south towards the mine with a 200-foot tunnel on the left and the open cut above on the hilltop. D.B. Sterrett, *U.S. Geological Survey*, 197.

The Royal Blue mine, showing the entrance to the 200-foot tunnel leading to the open cut above. D.B. Sterrett, *U.S. Geological Survey*, 198.

The Royal Blue mine, looking northeast across the open cut and showing the car on the track of the 200-foot tunnel. D.B. Sterrett, *U.S. Geological Survey*, 199.

Considering the value of production, it is rather surprising no one paid the $500 property taxes for the year that had been assessed to William Petry. The property reverted to the county in 1910 for unpaid taxes and remained in the receivership of the treasurer until 1915. There are several possible reasons for this. First, although the Royal Blue was producing turquoise and the tourmaline market was strong, other parts of Tannenbaum's financial empire were not prospering and he was always overextending himself. This strategy had worked in the past, but he reached a point where he was unable to balance all of his financial obligations.

In 1907 he was indicted for placing the sale proceeds of a bond issue of the Himalaya Mining Company in the personal account of his wife. Although it appears he was able to make restitution, this was only the first of a series of setbacks. The Kingsland Brick Company went bankrupt in June 1907 while he was treasurer. The Himalaya Mining Company made several internal changes to its management in 1909, including adding a new director, Julius Goldsmith. The financial crisis continued and in August 1910, L. Tannenbaum and Co.

declared bankruptcy, listing debts of $250,000 and assets of $20,000. This could have been one of the reasons Goldsmith left the Royal Blue, which ceased operations at that time. Tannenbaum may have thought continued sales of tourmaline would allow the Himalaya Mining Company to continue, but the collapse of the Chinese market in 1912 ended that hope.

Everything spiraled down from there. Lippman's wife Rachel passed away in April 1912, and he was forced to sell at auction everything he owned, including his home on the upper West Side and all other possessions. Six months after the auction, on December 1, 1914, Julius Lippman Tannenbaum died at age 63.

Tiffany at Tonopah

The name Tiffany looms large in fact and fiction throughout The Great American Turquoise Rush. This is especially true in the ongoing association of Tiffany with Nevada turquoise, although it is clear neither Charles L. Tiffany nor Tiffany and Co. ever had any investment in turquoise mining in Nevada other than they may have purchased turquoise produced from these mines.

As stated earlier, when Charles Lewis Tiffany died in1902, his son Louis Comfort Tiffany began moving Tiffany and Co. in a direction that fit his interest in design and glass production. The involvement of the elder Tiffany with the ATC in Cerrillos was covered in Chapter 2. Certainly neither the company nor the estate was interested in pursuing ownership of turquoise mines, although they would have continued to purchase turquoise, either unfinished for their own jewelry design or as finished jewelry.

When Lippman Tannenbaum began operations in Mesa Grande mining tourmaline, the market demand came largely from the worldwide prestige of Tiffany and Co. and the large orders it was receiving presumably from the Dowager Empress of China. To meet this demand, they purchased material from many sources. Tannenbaum was misidentified as an agent of Tiffany and Co. in this regard, and the association continued to his turquoise operations. It is likely that Tannenbaum did nothing to deny this association in order to avail himself of the marketing advantage of being associated with such a well-known brand. In this regard, Tannenbaum and the Himalaya Mining Company were not alone—Tiffany and Co. was alleged to own and operate mines that the Toltec Gem Mining Company in Crescent Peak owned.

The press supported these myths: "Old Crescent Camp, Oct. 25 – The famous turquoise diggings[23] are to be worked again by Tiffany and Company of

New York, who will take out 500 pounds of the finest gems of this kind in the world."

NEVADA TURQUOISE MINED BY TIFFANY. Property Near Miller Said To Produce $4,000 to $7,000 a Week. This mine is owned by the great jewelry firm of Tiffany and Company, of New York and J. Tannenbaum who holds the position of president of the Himalaya Mining Company. Ten men find steady employment at the mine and more will be employed as fast as room can be made for them. The buildings which have been erected by the company represent a cost of over $3,000 and have been nicely painted. All improvements are of a most substantial and enduring character.[24]

Anyone who has visited the Royal Blue mine site in recent times would be hard-pressed to envision the ramshackle "Tiffany" cabin as enduring, but these reports demonstrate how the myth of Tiffany ownership was created in the area. More surprising is the persistence of the myth to this day, although we can easily attribute that to the same incentive that existed in the early 1900s—the desire to maximize the Tiffany brand for marketing purposes. In an interview in 1976, C.T. Johnson, who later worked the Royal Blue and was closely associated with Lee Hand from the 1920s on, said:

The first big operation on the Royal Blue was the Himalaya Mining Company of Denver. (Actually it was an Arizona corporation with offices in New York, but they may have shipped turquoise on the railroad through Denver). At that time everyone termed it the "Tiffany" mine. Tiffany was the most abused name for turquoise mines in the west. If a person had ever sent a piece of turquoise to Tiffany's in New York, why it automatically would become a Tiffany mine. I sat down and wrote Tiffany's a letter one day, and as far as they knew they never owned a mine or never intended to own property! So anyway, for a long time it was known as the Tiffany mine, but it was actually the Himalaya Mining Company doing it. They had a colored gentleman (J. Goodman Braye) who was foreman of the operation, a top man, and they shipped several hundred pounds per month to Denver, not completely cleaned, but having just had a hammer to it to take off all the rock possible. They had built a real nice house on the property. I guess it is still standing there at the Royal Blue. When I took over, I built one and then fixed up the main one.[25]

Royal Blue turquoise. Private collection. Photo courtesy Michael Gomez and Teena Lee Ryan.

Ambush and Murder

George Simmons was a successful prospector. In addition to being a founding shareholder of the Toltec Gem Mining Company, which had mines at Crescent Peak and Halloran Springs, he also had interests in gold and silver. When the Toltec was formed, Simmons hired William Petry, a German lapidary who had worked with the Kley family of lapidaries in Denver, to set up a lapidary shop onsite so the Toltec could ship finished stones, thus eliminating the extra cost of that process, and sell directly to jewelry wholesalers. Simmons served as manager of the mining operations from the inception of the company sometime in 1898 and for a year or so according to Morrissey. During that time he hired William L. Miller, a well-known local miner, to serve as foreman of the mining crew. We don't know exactly when or if Simmons left his position as manager at Crescent Peak, but we know he was involved in other successful mining ventures, including the Emma and Big Tiger gold mines in the district.

Morrissey reported Simmons left after selling his shares about a year after the company began operations, but other sources claimed that as late as June 1903 he was still a shareholder in the company with the Wood brothers and John Lamont.[26] Morrissey claimed that Simmons' replacement, Milton Mundy, was "not very good" and that Wood had enlisted Simmons to return as manager of the mine in 1903.[27] In all likelihood Simmons had remained in a management capacity with the Toltec over the entire period, but was asked in 1903 to put more time into managing the Crescent Peak properties. Mundy filed the annual assessment for many of the Toltec claims on January 31, 1901 for the previous year of 1900 and for the Solitaire on December 31, 1903.

On October 15, 1903, Simmons was in Barnwell, California, a railhead on the California and Nevada state line that served the mining district as a transport hub. He was with a Mr. C.C. Smithson, another local miner. Smithson was reputed to have a checkered past. Before he turned to mining, he had been tried on multiple occasions on charges of stealing cattle. In each instance, he was acquitted.[28] William L. Miller had served as foreman at the Toltec mines and was close to Simmons. Miller must have been a trusted employee earlier because W.L. Miller was a witness to the filing of the location of the Solitaire claim by J.B. Wood on January 2, 1902. The events that unfolded that day demonstrated the deterioration of the relationship.

According to eye witness reports from Smithson and George W. Rose presented at the preliminary hearing on October 17, Miller met Simmons and Smithson while they were leaving Brown's store and nodded a greeting. He then went immediately through the back door of the store to get his 30 caliber rifle. Simmons and Smithson stopped at Earl's store to buy cigars, and then started out for the camp:

> Miller came trotting after them, rifle in hand. He called to them and Simmons stopped and alighted from the wagon to speak to him, with the reins still in his hands. Miller said, "I've got you two -------- now!" Simmons replied pleasantly, "Why, Billie Miller, put up your gun and talk with me." Miller replied by shooting. The first shot missed Simmons, struck the ground behind him and startled the horses, jerking one rein out of his hand. Simmons stumbled along trying to catch the rein and caught the tug. Miller than shot again, killing him instantly. He stumbled along a foot or two and fell.[29]

The account in the *Los Angeles Herald* described how Simmons and Miller had once been close, "inseparable friends" who were "absolutely fearless and would take more pleasure in helping a friend out of trouble than in helping himself," which seemed to include backing each other up in armed confrontations over mining rights. Something caused the relationship to sour. Perhaps it was Simmons' marriage. Miller's wife had died years earlier, and he may have resented the end to Simmons' bachelor days. More likely was a reputed dispute over water rights. Although Simmons had fired Miller sometime prior, they had once claimed the same water rights, but Miller's interest passed to E.C. Greening. Greening and Simmons shared the rights jointly.

Miller had no representation at the hearing and had surrendered peacefully immediately after the murder. He made an astute decision when he chose attorneys Frank R. Daley and H.W. Nisbett of San Bernardino. Their defense was insanity, and on February 25, 1904, the jury brought a verdict of not guilty by reason of insanity. The defense presented its case on the basis that Miller's hatred of Simmons was due to his belief he had ownership interest in properties owned by Simmons. Testimony at the trial showed this was not the case, and this was sufficient to allow the jury to conclude it had to be irrational for him to take such action when he clearly had no basis of ownership in the property, including water rights.[30] Miller was remanded to the care of his daughter, but quickly moved to Tonopah, Nevada, where he formed a partnership with his former associate, William Petry, owning and working the Royal Blue.

"Beautiful Woman's Beautiful Jewel"

When The Great American Turquoise Rush began in 1890, one of the principle reasons for the desire to secure and produce turquoise from the Southwest was the similarity in quality compared with Persia. The factors that limited production in Persia in the late 1880s caused the price of its turquoise to rise in Europe and the United States. Skeptics may conclude the main incentive for Kunz's 1892 about face on the quality of southwest turquoise was due to his position with Tiffany and Co. and the company's need for a cheaper source of turquoise rather than a change in his gemological assessment. The Great American Turquoise Rush was on, and companies from New York vied to establish economic dominance in the southwest turquoise market.

By the middle of the first decade of the twentieth century, the turquoise boom was slowing down. Although sales remained strong, change was indicated. The new century brought a sense of a changing world. Technological advances were affecting the lives of Americans, and economic prosperity had introduced the development of a new class of economic consumers, the middle class, which was driving the colossal U.S. economic engine. A good example of this was a lawsuit brought by the Arizona Turquoise Company in 1915 against a vacuum cleaner retailer. The claimants stated the cleaning demonstrations in the front display window they shared attracted large crowds interested in this new technological marvel and limited access to their store. The old ways were changing. The western United States, which had been considered a rugged, untamed frontier for most of the preceding century, was becoming settled and governed under rule of law rather than the frontier justice that had often been the norm. Culture and society began to reflect these changes. Women's fashions were turning from the straight-laced Victorian conventions to new ideas of openness and creativity.

We see these changes reflected in two distinct turquoise sales and marketing efforts at the time. In Chapter 6 we saw how both the Arizona Turquoise Company and the Southwest Turquoise Company issued catalogs promoting matrix turquoise as more desirable than the traditional non-matrix, sky blue turquoise. This was done because these companies were facing a problem confronted by every company operating during that time—no one could find enough of the non-matrix blue to meet the demand of fashion dictates.

Turquoise is formed from the combination of other mineral elements that must be combined in a precise manner under exacting conditions to create it and the other hydrous aluminum phosphates, including variscite, faustite, and chalcosiderite. It forms as both nodules and in veins, and contains the host rock of its formation. Turquoise is rare, and most of what is found will contain that host matrix often in beautiful combination. To utilize this matrix material required a change in demand from non-matrix, sky blue to an appreciation of the more available matrix turquoise in a variety of colors ranging from sky blue to dark blue and various shades of green. These companies needed to develop a market for matrix.

In addition to the supply imperative, another major contributor to this marketing effort was the recognition of a new phenomenon in the United States, tourism. During the previous century, most Americans were too preoccupied with the challenges of making a living to consider the idea of a vacation consisting of anything more than perhaps a Sunday outing. Those who did travel were wealthy individuals usually focused on a grand European holiday. The opening of the West by the railroads brought new economic opportunity and an influx of tourists eager to see the Wild West up close and to secure mementos of their visit. Thus the curios market was created, which we will look at more closely in the next chapter.

Some have suggested The Great American Turquoise Rush ended because the market was flooded with matrix turquoise, and this oversupply caused prices to drop. In reality, the turquoise boom ended for the most basic of reasons—demand crashed when the overall economy was devastated by the financial crisis of 1907 and the resulting recession of 1908. Combined with changing fashion trends that brought a drop in demand, the price of turquoise collapsed. With no economic incentive to extract, process, and market the stone, companies ceased production and the turquoise market became pretty much dormant for a number of years.

In contrast to the marketing efforts of the companies working in the Arizona Mineral Park area, the companies primarily involved in California and Nevada continued to base their production and marketing efforts on the old established turquoise look, the classic non-matrix, sky blue turquoise. The following examples from a 1905 catalog of the Toltec Gem Mining Company provide an example of this. Both the images and the accompanying text reflect status and a Victorian sense of pride and place. The first page of the catalog featured the slogan, "Beautiful Woman's Beautiful Jewel," establishing an image of privilege, elegance, and grace with a color lithograph image (this was long before the era of color photography was used in advertising), displaying a beautiful woman wearing a long string of perfectly matched, flawless, pale blue turquoise beads with a matching pin of a large turquoise cabochon set with a ring of diamonds. The following page supported this image, claiming, "The Perfect Turquoise, a Matchless Gem" under another string of elegantly calibrated, flawless turquoise beads, each of the desired Persian blue. The text accompanying the images reinforced this. Turquoise was referred to as the "true aristocrat" of gemstones. Whereas pearls have a sense of purity, and diamonds their sparkle, it is turquoise that "is a gem of gentility—modest yet beautiful in its soft, lustrous coloring—a stone which lends itself admirable to the uses of the fastidious." The catalog expresses that turquoise "enjoys an unusual vogue among cultured people" who are assumed to have the developed sense of class and taste to appreciate the unique qualities of fine turquoise. The sentiment is summed up in the sentence, "The turquoise will never become 'common'—it will remain the aristocrat."[31]

Toltec advertisement in *Cosmopolitan* magazine, 1905.

THE
TOLTEC TURQUOISE
A MATCHLESS GEM

TOLTEC

T

TRADE MARK

TOLTEC GEM MINING CO
CHAS. F. WOOD & CO. SELLING AGENTS

NEW YORK   CHICAGO

Toltec Gem Mining Company brochure cover page, 1905.

"Beautiful Woman's Beautiful Jewel," Toltec brochure, 1905.

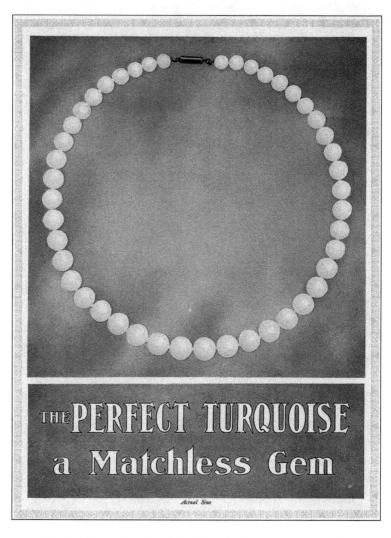

Actual Size

"Perfect Turquoise, Matchless Gem," Toltec brochure, 1905.

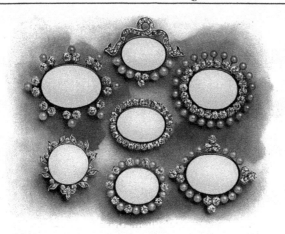

Actual Size

Actual Size

turquoise will never become "common"—it will remain the aristocrat.

In the past it has been extremely difficult to secure perfect turquoise. There have been on the market many cheap, inferior stones, deficient in formation and in color. There have also been marketed quantities of cheap imitations of an altogether worthless

"Turquoise will never become common," Toltec brochure, 1905.

laces, brooches, bracelets, rings, and
in fact, for high-grade jewelry of all
kinds. It is now possible to secure
necklaces of any desired length formed
of perfectly matched turquoise—truly
beautiful and unique ornaments. The

Toltec turquoise is also largely used for the center
stone of brooches, surrounded by diamonds and
pearls. This combination of the blue with the white
is very artistic and attractive—the brilliance of the
diamond and the soft, glowing white of the pearl

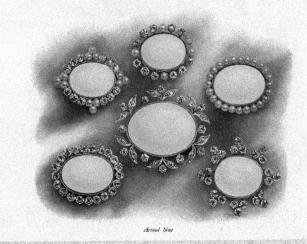

Actual Size

"Turquoise, Diamonds, and Pearls," Toltec brochure, 1905.

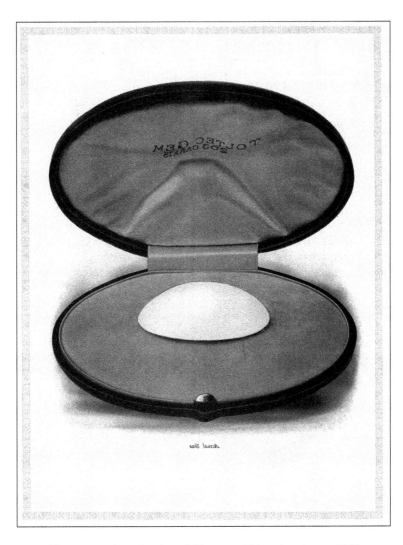

Giant turquoise cabochon, 210 carats, Toltec brochure, 1905.

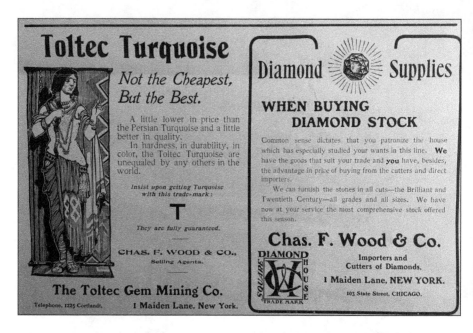

Toltec Gem Mining Company turquoise with Charles F. Wood and Co. diamond advertisement, around 1905. The marketing strategy first begun by the Azure Mining Company 10 years earlier continued with competing companies promoting their trademarks and guarantees.

By 1908, just three years after this catalog was published, the Southwest Turquoise Company began their catalog with a clear statement of their intended market:

> Los Angeles and many other western cities are fast becoming the abiding place for a part of the year at least, of the tourist and it is our desire to assist both the dealers and our visitors to know and appreciate the best in gems and jewelry.[32]

Although the company must have had some sense of changing trends given they included a long list of various gemstones for purchase, they had a clear idea about what was best when it came to turquoise and it differed from the picture the Toltec catalog painted just three years before: "The matrix turquoise is the most popular on account of the beautiful marking. The stones are like beautiful dream pictures and no two are alike." They went further in specifying which of the matrix was the most desirable: "The 'cobweb turquoise' surpasses all other in its beautiful markings. This is very rare as there is only one mine which has this particular quality."[33] It would come as no surprise to hear this sort of description used in current turquoise marketing efforts.

In the next chapter we will see how The Great American Turquoise Rush marked the end of one era of turquoise in the United States but ushered in a new era in how turquoise was mined, processed, distributed, marketed, and sold.

Colorado

Much fine turquoise was produced from mines in Colorado, but it did not play a role in The Great American Turquoise Rush. Although there were claims located in Colorado during the period, companies invested less than in other areas because of the lack of non-matrix, sky blue turquoise. As fashion changed, interest in Colorado's turquoise—which ranged from matrix blue to green—increased, and much more of the gemstone was brought to market.

The first mention of turquoise in Colorado was by J. Alden Smith in 1870, when he claimed he had obtained specimens from the southern part of the state cut and drilled by Indians and worn as a bracelet.[34] As in other areas in the Southwest where turquoise was discovered, the lack of market interest and low price eliminated any incentive to mine it. This began to change as it did elsewhere during the 1890s. Although there were other turquoise producing areas in the state including Villa Grove, Leadville, and Cripple Creek, these were not developed until later in the twentieth century. The first deposits and the center of mining activity at the turn of the century were near La Jara in Conejos County in south central Colorado.

The story of the development of turquoise during The Great American Turquoise Rush in the other areas was one of competing corporate interests, largely from New York, attempting to establish economic dominance over the market. The story in Colorado differed in that at the time it featured migration and the Gospel. Joseph Smith founded the Church of Jesus Christ of Latter Day Saints, also known as the Mormon Church, in 1830 in New York. In 1838, Jedidiah Grant established a community of Mormons in North Carolina, and their descendants moved to the high desert plateau of the Rocky Mountains looking for economic opportunity and a place to preach the Gospel. The first Mormon settlers began to arrive in 1879 as the railroad opened southern Colorado. Others followed a similar path, and the area became a Mormon stronghold. Extended families continued in the lapidary and mining business, many to the present day, including the King, Smith, Edgar, Otteson, Gibson, and McGinnis families.

According to Bill King, great grandson of I.P. King, Israel Pervoise King came to Manassa in 1894 from North Carolina with his family. While searching for minerals, he came across indications of a prehistoric Indian turquoise mine. In 1895, he filed claim on the Lick Skillet, so named because the family was so poor they licked the skillet after every meal. Bill King gave a glimpse into the lack of capital for investment in the mine when he related how a local doctor in partnership with I.P. sent his patients to the mine to work off their bills. They took turquoise to Santa Fe, a major turquoise production area at the time, but encountered little interest. It wasn't until much later that production at the Lick Skillet, renamed the King's Manassa mine, increased under the direction of I.P.'s son Charles and his son Pete, Bill's father.[35]

According to *Harvey and Harvey*, in 1890 I.P. King and his son Charles discovered the largest and most well-known turquoise deposit in Colorado 13 miles south of La Jara and a mile and half west of the Rio Grande River. They did not work the mine because the value did not warrant it at the time. They staked 12 claims in 1900 and worked the annual assessments. At some point, "leading men in the valley" formed the Colorado Mining Company.[36] According to Sterrett in the 1908 Precious Gems section of *MRUS*, the company leased the mine to C.G. King of Manassa, Colorado and C.H. Wyman and H.E. James of Colorado Springs, who set up a lapidary to cut turquoise at Colorado Springs.[37] The mine produced a handsome turquoise matrix stone with colors of dark to light blue and greenish-blue and continued to produce throughout the next decade and, with some periods of inactivity, into the present day.

In the 1916 report of *MRUS*, published in 1919, W.T. Schaller, who had followed D.B. Sterrett as editor of the chapter on gemstones, stated the value of turquoise produced in 1916 was about double the amount of any of the previous four years, with Nevada as the largest producer followed by Colorado. He also cited the following description of the turquoise mine near Manassa, Conejos County, Colorado made by E.S. Larsen of the United States Geographical Survey in which he said the mine was owned by C.G. King and had been worked for the last 10 or 12 years, either on a lease by shares or for cash. He made an interesting observation that the turquoise mined was largely sold or traded to Indians.[38]

As we saw at Mineral Park, efforts continued at the very end of The Great American Turquoise Rush to market matrix turquoise as a desirable alternative. This made sense from an economic standpoint—far more matrix turquoise ranging from green to blue, including the traditional sky blue, was extracted. Cutting cabochons in matrix allowed larger pieces to be used in jewelry design, in contrast to the small, non-matrix pieces that had to be set with companion pearls and other precious gems. The 1908 catalogs of the Arizona Turquoise Company and the Southwest Turquoise Company indicated the effort to develop this new market for matrix turquoise. Although the Arizona Turquoise Company consumer continued to be based on the east coast, the Southwest Turquoise Company introduced a new target customer, the southwest tourist.

The Schaller report showed that by 1916 turquoise production had increased in Nevada and Colorado, areas where matrix turquoise was being discovered, and decreased in the states that formerly led production: New Mexico, Arizona, and California. Also very important was the new market that had developed for turquoise, the American Indians of the southwest. As we will see in the next chapter, this was an important development not only for the direction turquoise production would follow, but also for the development of Native American jewelry.

Looking north towards the Colorado Turquoise Mining Company Mine, Conejos County, 13 miles southeast of La Jara. The mine shafts are near the office to the right on the hill. D.B. Sterrett, *U.S. Geological Survey*, 127.

Notes

1. *Salt Lake Herald*, June, 22, 1903.
2. Ibid.
3. *Jewelers Circular*, "Death of John R. Wood," February 9, 1898, 25.

4. *The Jewelers Review,* April 19, 1899, 509.
5. G.F. Kunz, *Gems, Jewelers' Materials, and Ornamental Stones of California,* San Francisco: California State Mining Bureau, 1905, 107.
6. L.M. Vredenburgh, *History of Mining in the Halloran Hills, Shadow Mountains, and Silurian Hills* San Bernardino: 1996.
7. M.J. Rogers, "Report of an Archeological Reconnaissance in the Mohave Sink Region," *Archeology,* vol.1, no. 1, The San Diego Museum, February 1929, 4.
8. E. Nazelrod, "Turquoise—Inside and Out, Part Two," *Lapidary Journal,* January 1985, 1304.
9. M.J. Rogers, 5.
10. "Long Lost Mines of Precious Gems Are Found Again," *The San Francisco Call,* March 18, 1898, 2.
11. Ibid., "Wonderful Find," March 19, 1898, 16.
12. Rogers, 1.
13. N.N. Leonard III and C.E. Drover, "Prehistoric Turquoise Mining in the Halloran Springs District, San Bernardino County, California," *Journal of California and Great Basin Anthropology,* vol.2, 1980, 252.
14. Mineral Certificates no. 299, 300, 301, 302, General Land Office.
15. D.E. Russell, *Gem Cutting in Gem Cove,* City of Glen Cove, 1919.
16. M.I. Jacobson, "Lippman Tannenbaum Part II," *Mineral News,* October 2010, 6.
17. Hoffman, "On the Minerology of Nevada," *USGS,* vol. 4, Bulletin no. 3, 1878, 740.
18. B. Silliman, *Engineering and Mining Journal,* September 10, 1882, 169.
19. G.F. Kunz, *Gems and Precious Stones of North America,* New York: The Scientific Publishing Company, 1890.
20. J.E. Pogue, *The National Academy of Sciences,* vol. xii, 1915, 50.
21. Nye County Recorder, Book 1, 370–375.
22. F.R. Morrissey, "Turquoise Deposits of Nevada," Nevada Bureau of Mines, Report 17, 25.
23. *Los Angeles Herald,* vol. 36, no. 25, October 26, 1908, 10.
24. *Inter-Mountain Republican,* December 4, 1908.
25. "The Old Timer, An Interview In Depth," *Turquoise Annual,* vol. 1, 1976, 15.
26. Salt Lake Herald, June 6, 1903.
27. F.R. Morrissey, 7.
28. "George Simmons, Manager of Toltec Gem Mining Company, Ambushed and Killed by Miner," *Los Angeles Herald,* October 16, 1903.
29. "Miller Held For Desert Tragedy," *Los Angeles Herald,* October 17, 1903.
30. "William L. Miller Found Not Guilty," *Los Angeles Herald,* February 26, 1904.
31. Toltec Gem Mining Company, Catalog, 1905.
32. Southwest Turquoise Company, Catalog, 1908, 1.
33. Ibid., 5.
34. R.M. Pearl, "Gem Mining in Colorado," *The Colorado Magazine,* November 1939, 219.
35. Bill King, *History of King's Manassa Mine,* Durango Silver Company, 2016, www.durango silver.com
36. J.R. Harvey and R. Harvey, "Turquoise Among the Indians and a Colorado Turquoise Mine," *Colorado Magazine,* v.15, 1938, 189–190.
37. D.B. Sterrett, *Mineral Resources of the United States,* 1908, 781.
38. W.T. Schaller, *Mineral Resources of the United States, Part 2,* 1916 (1919), 895.

8

An Ending and a New Beginning

Price and Value

During The Great American Turquoise Rush, prospectors relocated various prehistoric American Indian turquoise mines. Investors, primarily from New York City and involved in the jewelry trade, bought claims and established mining companies with the intent of developing as much control of the turquoise market as they could. These savvy businesspeople knew the company with the most control over supply could influence price and maximize profits. Mining experts were hired to supervise the local operations and oversee the miners who would extract and sort the turquoise. The turquoise was shipped to lapidaries, primarily on the east coast but also in Denver and Chicago, where it was cut into cabochons to be set in jewelry. Wholesale jewelers fabricated pieces they sold to retail outlets throughout the United States, Canada, and Europe. Some companies maintained as many of these functions as possible to vertically integrate the various stages of production, which produced the highest profit margins at each stage.

Although we have tried to present a carefully detailed explanation of the characters involved in The Great American Turquoise Rush, with attention to well-documented support of their involvement, reviewing the price of turquoise can help increase understanding about the rise and subsequent fall in the demand. In any study of the price of a product, commodity, or service, it is important to know the difference between price and value. The price is what a buyer is willing to pay; value is what something is worth. Although these two are linked, they are not the same. Price is a function of supply and demand. With demand constant, the less supply the higher the price and, conversely, the more supply the lower the price. Assuming constant supply, the greater the demand, the higher the price; the lower the demand, the lower the price. Value is primarily determined by the cost of production.

Economists tend to believe these factors operate in a perfect theoretical fashion, as they seek the perfect rational combination of price and value. Those who have been involved in any market know that is seldom the case. Markets comprise people, and we humans are decidedly irrational at times, guided by our emotions as much as our intellect. Two emotions that most affect price are greed and fear. Consumers and investors hungry for profits or desiring possession often pay a price significantly above the intrinsic value of the coveted item. When they become fearful that prices might plummet with no buyers available at any price, a shrewd investor or consumer can take advantage of a scenario where prices are well below value, then sell when the price is well above value and others cannot wait to pay even higher prices in their greedy pursuit of gain.

Unlike a commodity such as precious metals or agricultural products that sell almost exclusively based on the lowest cost producer, turquoise has only one use—it is a semi-precious gemstone to be collected or used in jewelry. Fashion demand's unique factors are not connected to other supply and demand influences. When The Great American Turquoise Rush began in 1890, the fashion dictates of the time influenced the price of turquoise. They also presented market challenges that contributed to the end of the boom.

Before reviewing the turquoise price and production numbers during The Great American Turquoise Rush, it will be useful to understand how it is mined and how production is similar to, but also different from, other mining operations. Prospectors looking for turquoise discovered few of the mines featured here. Rather they were actively seeking deposits of gold, silver, and copper. When they found turquoise deposits, they had no incentive to stake claims because of the low price. This changed when Kunz made his proclamation in 1892 and drove up the price.

Turquoise mining differs in several ways from precious metal mining. First, turquoise is usually found close to the surface within a zone of 10 to 60 feet, although there are exceptions to this rule. Second, the goal of miners in extracting the metals is to locate and remove the ore containing the highest concentrations of the mineral, and then extracting the metal from the rock. They do this through a combination of physical crushing and mechanical and chemical processing, resulting in pure metal for market. In contrast, the turquoise miner must be as careful as possible during extraction not to damage the precious gemstone.

The coal or precious metal miner locates the deposit by drilling core samples, and then follows the vein into the mountain and moves up or down as the ore provides. The first access is often a horizontal adit or entrance, but because it is much easier to move heavy ore rock on a flat surface than up or down, an ore body becomes a maze of tunnels honeycombing below, or above the main entrance. Turquoise generally forms close to the surface, requiring a different mining process. The blasting used to break up the rock face must be done in a gentler manner to preserve the turquoise. After removal, the ore rock must be sorted and graded to identify the turquoise and determine the various grades.

Turquoise is relatively soft, and it is estimated that at least 80 percent of it is too soft or chalky to cut successfully for jewelry without having the stone cracking or absorbing oils and changing color. From the earliest days of production, this problem has been addressed by treating rough turquoise to increase the hardness and protect or enhance the color. The 20 percent of turquoise not requiring some form of treatment to be commercially viable also comes in a range of grades, with perhaps only the top 5 percent considered high-grade and only 1 to 2 percent considered true gem grade. Natural (untreated) high-grade turquoise is among the most rare of all gemstones, certainly far above diamonds, and gem-grade the rarest of the rare.

Contending with these factors was challenging in and of itself for miners, but their efforts were complicated even more by the demand for only non-matrix, sky blue turquoise. All turquoise, regardless of source, ranges in color from green to blue. The nature of the stone is relative to the host rock that provided the source elements for its formation—meaning matrix is an essential part of turquoise. Limiting marketable material to only one color with no matrix meant limited supply, driving the price high. It also meant turquoise meeting these criteria were often very small, difficult to cut pieces with settings limited to clusters with other gemstones.

In Chapter 2 we saw the production amounts published in the official USGS *MRUS* annual report. These estimates most likely are low because mine owners were motivated to underreport production amounts: (1) If the claim were patented, those numbers were used to asses property tax; (2) Miners were naturally private about their affairs. They did not want the competition knowing their business and were wary of high-graders—trespassers intending to steal the best turquoise from the mine—and claim jumpers who might try to over-claim their mine. Often a company claimed multiple mines surrounding their main producing claim solely for the purpose of providing a buffer zone. This difference is apparent when comparing amounts reported by the USGS and those prepared by the governor of New Mexico in his mineral report.

Year	Total for all U.S. (USGS)	Total for New Mexico Only
1891	$150,000	$150,000
1892	$175,000	$175,000
1893	$143,000	$200,000
1894	$34,000	$250,000
1895	$50,000	$350,000
1896	$40,000	$475,000

According to the USGS report, from 1883 until 1888 annual production ranged between $2,000 and $3,500. In 1889, the amount jumped significantly to $23,675 and was a bit higher in 1890 at $28,675. The following are the annual U.S. production amounts from 1891 to 1921:

1891 – $150,000	1907 – $23,840
1892 – $175,000	1908 – $147,950
1893 – $143,136	1909 – $179,273
1894 – $34,000	1910 – $85,900
1895 – $50,000	1911 – $44,751
1896 – $40,000	1912 – $10,140
1897 – $55,000	1913 – $8,075
1898 – $50,000	1914 – $13,370
1899 – $72,000	1915 – $11,691
1900 – $82,000	1916 – $21,811
1901 – $118,000	1917 – $14,171
1902 – $130,000	1918 – $20,667
1903 – $110,000	1919 – $17,700
1904 – $100,000	1920 – $4,869
1905 – $65,000	1921 – $1,450
1906 – $22,840	

In 1913 production dropped to $8,075 and for the rest of the decade ranged from $11,000 to $22,000. From 1923–1932 there are no production reports and, as expected, production during the Great Depression was low.

These numbers reveal several things. From 1890–1891, the first full year of production during The Great American Turquoise Rush, amounts increased by over 400 percent. They remained high through 1893, and then dropped dramatically. This was due to a serious economic downturn in 1893. Over 50,000 businesses failed, and over 500 banks went under. Production rebounded from 1895–1899, yet remained lower than the pre-crash highs, though significantly higher than before the turquoise boom began. Still, these numbers might be understated because based on the governor of New Mexico's mineral report, production was stronger during those years than the official peak numbers of 1909. Through the first decade of the twentieth century, production amounts fluctuated but remained strong, peaking in 1909, and a comparison of the value of money during The Great American Turquoise Rush with today's value, as well a similar comparison of production, confirms the magnitude.

Production in 1940 was reported at $20,000. By 1955, the only amount reported, $20,000, was from the Lone Mountain mine in Nevada, owned by Lee Hand. Interest in turquoise and American Indian jewelry increased during the 70s, 80s, and beyond, creating a boom in production during the 70s. No production numbers were reported in the 1970s except for the years 1974–1977:

1974 – $2,000,000
1975 – $5,200,000
1976 – $3,900,000
1977 – $4,500,000

From 1978 until late 1980, only sporadic reports on turquoise production exist. This changed beginning in 1990:

1990 – $1,105,000
1991 – $ 611,000
1992 – $1,994,000
1993 – $3,040,000
1994 – $1,710,000

By the end of the 1990s, production had fallen to almost nothing but had begun to pick up by the middle of the decade, ranging around $450,000 annually through 2011. Then a new bull market in turquoise emerged that has continued to the present (2016), with production in 2011 of $1,330,000, 2012 of $1,320,000, and in 2013 $1,310,000. All production numbers come from the *MRUS* annual report on gemstones.

Although impressive on a nominal basis, the production numbers do not show the relative value of past production to current values. When we factor in the effect of inflation over the century since The Great American Turquoise

Rush, we see why that span must be considered the greatest turquoise production period in U.S. history. In 1894, production was at the low ebb of the entire period at $30,000, yet in 2016 dollars that would be about $822,000, assuming an annual inflation rate of 3 percent. At peak production in 1909, the equivalent dollar amount today would be about $4.2MM, which is three times current production amounts.

The only time comparable values have been produced since The Great American Turquoise Rush occurred between 1974 and 1977 and between 1990 and 1994. In today's dollars, 1993's peak would be worth over $6MM. The all-time record for turquoise production in the United States is 1975 at $5.2MM for all grades of turquoise, worth almost $17MM today. The booms of the 1970s and 1990s were short-lived compared with the two-decades-long Great American Turquoise Rush. The total official turquoise production of 1891 to 1909 was $1,743,699, with an average of $91,775 per year. This would be worth about $2.75MM in today's dollars. As stated earlier, these estimates are probably understated. Other estimates range from $4MM-8MM over the entire period, which at the lower amount would have been worth over $97MM today—or an annual average of over $6MM in current value.

Pogue stated the estimated value from Cerrillos alone at $2MM, and a former superintendent of the Azure mine in the Burros estimated production there at "several million dollars." This represented a wholesale price for rough turquoise, the total retail value of which was significantly higher. Pogue discussed retail prices in his 1915 monograph, *Turquois*. He stated cut turquoise from the Azure mine sold for $5 per carat in 1893. By 1903, the range was $5 to $10 per carat and by 1907, at the height of The Great American Turquoise Rush, high-grade, non-matrix, sky blue turquoise cabochons sold for between $6 and $25 per carat, with $15 per carat the average for good quality. That would be almost $450 in today's prices, which only the very finest gem-grade turquoise from a few select mines might achieve. The high price was a factor of demand, and only the non-matrix, sky blue turquoise was used, while turquoise with matrix sold for a fraction of the price. Pogue quotes price ranges for matrix during the period as 25 cents to one dollar per carat.[1] A rule of thumb for cutting turquoise is to expect a minimum of 50 percent waste from rough weight to finished cabochons. To obtain only the non-matrix, sky blue, waste must have been much higher.

We know the financial crisis of 1907 and the resulting recession of 1908 reduced turquoise demand and signaled the end of The Great American Turquoise Rush. The insistence on high-grade turquoise restricted supply and kept prices high. Most importantly, fashion trends were moving away from the Victorian image of the nineteenth century to the more dynamic, modern world of the new twentieth century. Ironically for the future of turquoise, twentieth-century jewelry fashion was inspired by a vision from the past.

American Indian Jewelry: Curio to Craft to Fine Art

By the end of The Great American Turquoise Rush, it was clear mining companies were looking for a market for their turquoise with matrix. The Southwest Turquoise Company had promoted the beauty of the full range from blue to green, especially the matrix they referred to as "cobweb" in their 1908 catalog. Also that year, the Arizona Turquoise Company catalog extolled the beauty and versatility of matrix turquoise and displayed settings with much larger stones than they had previously produced using only the very small non-matrix, sky blue cabochons. The jewelry bore a close resemblance to what was available in the curio marketplace. In addition to promoting the full range of color and matrix, these companies were also attempting to reach the new tourism market the railroads enabled, which provided easy access and a quicker and more comfortable journey. The railroads brought economic expansion with increased mining exploration and the resulting commercial opportunities—banking, retail, and plenty of saloons for drinking, gambling, and other activities—that accompany a rapidly expanding economy. In addition, the repression of the Native American tribes made journey through the Southwest safer. Visitors were eager to bring home a souvenir representing the West's frontier days, and the curio market was introduced.

The story of American Indian jewelry is a complex combination of history, economics, art, and anthropology. Several important studies have been done on the subject. Following is a brief overview of how this developing market was influenced by turquoise during the twentieth century.

The Navajo learned to work with metal in the mid-1850s, but did not create silver work of note until their return from forced exile at Bosque Redondo in 1868, which they refer to as "The Long Walk." This work was represented by items such as buckles, bridles, buttons, and pins they needed as farmers and herders as well as items of adornment—necklaces, bracelets, and rings. The scarcity of money and jobs at the time led the Navajo to use their creations as collateral for credit at the reservation trading posts. They traded for items they needed and redeemed them at some future point. If someone defaulted on the loan, the trader kept the items as payment, also known as pawn. Thus the trading post played a key role in the development of both Indian jewelry and turquoise.

The developing American arts and crafts movement, combined with the expanding tourist market of the Southwest, contributed to the development of a market for American Indian jewelry on two paths, craft and curio. Craft was defined as the careful handmade design and production of a piece by one artist, whereas curio was a commercial endeavor using techniques to mass produce items not associated with any one individual.[2] The curio trade became a confluence of the two trends. On February 9, 1880, the first train arrived in Santa Fe. At the same time, Jake Gold, who had been in the dry goods business with his brother Aaron since the mid-1870s, opened Gold's Provision House with "Gold's Indian Pottery" on the portal above the entrance to the store on San Francisco Street.[3] Most of the pottery came from Cochiti Pueblo, and he also carried textiles. As the tourist trade developed, and demand increased for the curios, many buyers balked at the high price of Gold's finer handmade pottery and weavings. This led him to contract for cheaper, mass-produced items from non-native sources to include with the finer crafts. As the tourist market continued to expand and competition increased, pressure mounted to provide less expensive items, and mass-produced pieces began to crowd out the handmade craftwork.

Fred Harvey was an English immigrant who recognized the potential the expanding railroads provided. The first Harvey House was opened in Kansas in 1875, the main dining option for those heading west. Harvey expanded into lodging and selling souvenirs as a logical next step for the company and at the time of his death in 1901, the Harvey Company was a western institution with 15 hotels and 47 restaurants in 12 states. In 1902, Harvey's daughter Minnie and her husband J.F. Huckel created the Indian Department headed by Herman Schweitzer. It was Schweitzer's job to collect Native American arts and crafts for sale as souvenirs. According to Lidchi, the company was an active buyer and a reputable dealer, but by 1932, Huckel told Schweitzer, "We handle genuine it is true, but we handle phony as well."[4] In catering to the often-changing trends of consumer demand, the company acquired the best fine craftwork while also promoting mass-produced commercial items.

Much of Harvey's older, finer pieces consisted of the heavy style the Navajos favored and came from the unredeemed pawn at various trading posts. In response to tourist demand for lighter, less expensive jewelry, the company began to contract for mass-produced pieces that resembled the finer pieces but often not created by Native Americans. This created a defining conflict through the 1930s and on and continues to this day in the major tourist centers of the West. As long as the cheaper, mass-produced items are not represented as handmade by individual Native American artisans, the two can coexist, leaving the choice up to an informed consumer. As we might suspect, some will misrepresent the items in an attempt to increase demand and profit. This fraud is an ongoing challenge.

Although *Atsidi Chon* (Ugly Smith) is credited with being the first Navajo to set turquoise in silver, it is Slender Maker of Silver, younger brother of *Atsidi Sani* (Old Smith), generally considered the first Navajo to learn metalwork, that refined the techniques into a true expressive craft beginning in the 1890s. His son Fred Peshlakai expanded this expressive craft tradition in jewelry-making beginning in the 1920s and continuing until the 1950s. This innovative design flourished after World War II as a young generation took the traditions of the past and combined them with a unique, modern perspective to create jewelry as fine art. Names such as Lloyd Kiva New, Charles Loloma, Joe Quintana, Preston Monongye, Paul Saufkie, and Kenneth Begay forged a new direction followed by the next leaders in Native jewelry, including Jesse Monongya, Cippy Crazyhorse, Verma Nequatewa, Harvey Begay, and Lee Yazzie. Today there are hundreds of talented Native American artists continuing the jewelry tradition first begun by Slender Maker of Silver. Turquoise was a key component in the design of both curio and craft jewelry, and the demand from this growing market determined in large part the direction of turquoise mining and production following The Great American Turquoise Rush.

A central figure during the transition from the boom days of The Great American Turquoise Rush to the new role for turquoise in the production of American Indian jewelry for both the craft and curio market were those who operated the trading posts on the Indian Reservations. The Commissioner of Indian Affairs licensed the trading posts, which were monitored by local Indian agents. In 1875, seven trading posts were licensed on the Navajo Reservation alone. This number rose steadily after 1900, reaching 154 in 1930.

Traders served many roles. In the classic model they were the local general store, stocking staples and dry goods as well as other items like saddles, clothing, jewelry, and livestock feed. One of their most important functions was to extend credit to an often cash-poor community through the acceptance of jewelry as collateral. In this way, traders were bankers of sorts to a people that had no tradition of money in their culture. They were intermediaries for a culture attempting to integrate into the white man's world. Traders played a key role in jewelry production because they often provided the turquoise and silver necessary for the designs, and suggested styles and items the marketplace favored. They then assisted in bringing the jewelry to market. Today the term trading post has become generalized and may be applied to anything from a tourist shop to a convenience store.

Production adapted to meet the needs of a market that no longer demanded only non-matrix, sky blue turquoise. Matrix was regarded as an important part of grading, as was color ranging from green to blue. To meet the demand for handmade and mass-produced Indian jewelry, new treatment and systems of grading became a greater part of turquoise production.

Treating turquoise to either deepen the color or make it harder was not new. During The Great American Turquoise Rush, the Azure Mining Company used an effective marketing campaign when they guaranteed their trademarked gemstones would not change color. They were able to do this primarily because most of their turquoise came from the Elizabeth Pocket, which was known to produce hard turquoise more resistant to absorbing the oils that caused the color to fade or change, which was an issue with their competitors' gemstones. Hazel Doty, daughter of Joseph Doty, claims her father, as head of the Aztec Turquoise Company, used a special process that kept the stone from turning green and replaced any turquoise with the Aztec trademark that changed color.[5] L. Bradford Prince of the New Mexico Turquoise Company corresponded with people claiming they could improve turquoise through treatment.

Treating turquoise became a greater part of production following the invention of epoxy resins and the development of treatments to stabilize chalky stones by introducing the resin into it under pressure. From the 1950s on, this and other treatments to improve color and hardness have allowed the use of turquoise that previously was too soft or lacked enough color to be used in commercial jewelry production. The difference in price between natural turquoise, which has received no treatment of any kind, and treated turquoise, often referred to as stabilized, is substantial. It is estimated that up to 80 percent of all turquoise produced is too soft and pale to be used commercially unless it is treated for color or hardness or both. Several proprietary treatment processes have been developed, allowing for more to be brought to market at a much lower cost than would be the case with natural turquoise. In general, artisans prefer natural turquoise, whereas the mass producers use the much lower-cost stabilized product. The 1974 *MRUS* listed the wholesale price per pound for natural and treated turquoise from both the Kingman and Castle Dome mines:

Natural	Low-grade	Medium-grade	High-grade
Kingman	$80	$100–125	$200–250
Castle Dome	$80	$100–125	$150–200

Treated, cutting-grade turquoise:

Grade 1 – Blue $60
Grade 1 – Blue-Green $40
Grade 1 – Green $30

Colbaugh Processing, the largest turquoise producer in the United States, has the turquoise concession at Kingman. About 80 percent of everything they find requires their proprietary treatment, with only 20 percent natural. In today's market, the price per pound for natural Kingman rough runs from $450 for low-grade to $3,500 for high-grade, and a range for treated rough of $25 for low-grade to $1,500 for high-grade.[6] This difference in price for natural and stabilized turquoise has been reflected in the significant difference in retail prices for commercial, mass-produced, southwest-style jewelry and handcrafted, fine art Indian jewelry.

Another technique that followed the invention of epoxy resin was the use of this and other means to strengthen the turquoise, not by infusing the stone through some treatment while it is still rough, but by applying the agent to the back of the cut cabochon. This technique gained popularity during the late 1960s. One of the early innovators in this technique was Bill King, son of Pete King and great grandson of I.P. King, who first discovered the turquoise mines outside of Manassa, Colorado. The external backing provides strength to the stone but can be removed, allowing the turquoise to remain natural and untreated while reducing the chance of fracture. Both stabilizing rough turquoise and backing natural cut turquoise have allowed the market to expand and more fully utilize what is a rare stone and very costly to mine.

After the Rush

Although The Great American Turquoise Rush as we depict it covered the years 1890–1910, production did not commence in any significant way until 1892 and it continued beyond the recession of 1908 and our date of 1910. Isolated instances of turquoise mining took place throughout the second decade of the twentieth century; for all practical purposes, however, it was not until the mid-twenties that the growing market for Indian jewelry began to affect the demand and price. This development was different for each area.

Cerrillos

New Mexico was the epicenter of production during The Great American Turquoise Rush, but when the boom ended, production in the state soon came to an almost complete halt. The ATC produced little after 1907, and no turquoise mining crews have been hired in the area since 1915. James Patrick McNulty continued to live there and worked the mines somewhat in the 1920s. Vern Byrne extracted several hundred dollars' worth from the Blue Bell in the 1930s, as did Herculano Montayo from the Tiffany.[7] The ATC patent claims for the Tiffany and the Castilian were sold at some point in the 1920s or 1930s to the Gerards, a wealthy family of old east coast money active in many businesses, including natural resources. As the story goes the property was purchased as a wedding gift because Mr. Gerard thought owning a turquoise mine was a romantic gesture. The family never developed the mine and around 1980 sold the land and half-interest in the mineral rights to two developers from Amarillo, Frank Rapstine and D.E. "Skip" Stahl, who then sold to the current owner, Douglas Magnus, in the late 80s. Some small-scale miners maintain claims in the area and continue to produce turquoise.

Burro Mountains

The copper-rich ores of the Burro Mountains finished turquoise mining there. As the price of turquoise dropped during the first decade of the new century, the price of copper rose. In 1909, Thomas Parker sold his claims to Phelps Dodge for $2MM. As noted in Chapter 3, under the direction of Mabel Dodge, the company created, Tyrone, a model company town near the mines where the company provided homes, shops, schools, and health facilities for its workers. This paternalistic approach soon extended to other communities where the company had mining operations. The town was completed in 1915, and production driven by demand was active during the war years. Yet the boom was short-lived and the mines were abandoned in the early 1920s following the post-World War I depression of commodity prices and as lower cost production became available. The town of Tyrone became a ghost town, and the site was later destroyed as part of the Phelps Dodge development of the Tyrone open-pit copper mine, which began operation in 1969.

The Azure Mining Company had accumulated a large block of claims. After the turquoise boom ended, the company kept those claims. They continued in existence and, Gillerman reports, they were sold to Phelps Dodge in 1959 (Gillerman, NMBMMR, 1964:44). Yet the Azure Mining Company was voluntarily dissolved in 1956. Homer Milford speculates the claims were sold to someone else, and Phelps Dodge obtained them in 1959.

Following The Great American Turquoise Rush, little turquoise was mined because the old turquoise claims were owned primarily by large mining operations and many of the old mines were destroyed by other mining activity. In spite of these restrictions, some turquoise continues to be mined in the area, but on a very small scale. Robert H. Weber of the New Mexico Bureau of Mines reported in the 1976 *Turquoise Annual* that the Phelps Dodge Corporation still controlled the old turquoise properties and their recent open-pit copper mine had in recent years exposed turquoise and that this was being mined under contract by James Hamilton of Silver City doing business as Tyrone Turquoise with the turquoise coming from the Tiffany mine although, once again, the use of the name was unauthorized and used purely for marketing purposes.

Hachita and Jarilla

During The Great American Turquoise Rush, turquoise was mined in Hachita and the Jarilla Mountains. Since then only sporadic production has taken place, and the turquoise has never been of the highest quality from either area. Currently author Philip Chambless manages claims in Hachita. As in the Burros, much of this area is leased for mineral exploration to large natural resource companies. Weber reported in the 1976 *Turquoise Annual* that at the time the Cameo mine was registered as an open-pit operation by Brian Bell of Silver City, although no production figures were cited.

Courtland

Of all the regions that mined turquoise during The Great American Turquoise Rush, Courtland, Nevada, and Colorado were the primary sources to a growing American Indian jewelry market, yet Courtland is almost completely forgotten today. As we saw in Chapter 5, Nick Rascom sold the majority of his claims to Thomas Parker and, in 1904, to George Good. Good mined the claims for some years, but they then passed to L.D. Shattuck, who had begun to acquire claims from Rascom in 1906, and who was the principal owner of turquoise claims on Turquoise Mountain by the middle of the next decade. Shattuck either leased a claim or sold to Joseph Baldwin Tanner, most likely at or around 1920.

Tanner was the son of Seth Tanner, an early pioneer of the Arizona Territory that Brigham Young sent to settle in northern Arizona. Seth Tanner was known among the Navajo as *Hosteen Shush* "Mr. Bear", and was one of the first of many prominent Mormons involved in the trading post business that included the Burnham, Foutz, and McGee families. Joseph Baldwin Tanner, who was known to the Navajo as *Shush Yazzhi,* "Little Bear," spoke Navajo, Hopi, Zuni, and Tewa and was a close friend to Chee Dodge, the first tribal president after the Navajo reorganized their tribal governance. According to Joseph E. Tanner, Joseph Baldwin's grandson and owner of Tanner's Indian Arts in Gallup, Seth and Joseph Baldwin mined and also set up several Indian trading posts. Joe mined the turquoise then took the stone and silver to the Navajo, Hopi, Zuni, and Santo Domingo bead and jewelry makers. They kept half the finished goods and Joe took half, though he often tried to buy from the Indians.

The Tanners and other traders like them sold the beads and jewelry at their trading posts and also wholesaled them to other retail sellers.[8] We know Joseph Baldwin Tanner was mining in Courtland in 1928 because Joe E. Tanner tells of his uncle sharing with him how, as a young boy in 1928, he went with Grandpa Joe to mine turquoise in Courtland in what they called the "Tanner Tunnel," which he had been doing for some years at that time. In Joe E. Tanner's opinion, Joseph Baldwin Tanner was instrumental in the marriage of turquoise and silver in early Native American jewelry and some of the best ever made was crafted during the 1910s and 1920s.

Joseph Baldwin Tanner in turn leased his claim at Courtland to C.G. Wallace, probably in the early 1930s. Wallace would eventually own the "Last Chance" mine at Courtland. Wallace had begun working for Charles Kelsey at Zuni in 1919 and was operating his own trading post in 1928, with a workshop in the back for native silversmiths. He continued to provide turquoise, silver, and design suggestions to the artisans, and then marketed their finished products. This arrangement with the larger producers like the Harvey Company and the many trading posts nurtured the developing Native American jewelry market.

There is reference to T.E. Kelso mining the Avalon claim he had bought from Lynn Shattuck during the 1930s and selling the turquoise through Petty's

Indian Trading Post in Tucson, but the authors were not able to ascertain the existence of this establishment.[9] According to Smith, the turquoise market remained steady during the 1930s, with buyers from Los Angeles, Albuquerque, and Gallup.

By the 1950s, turquoise mining in Courtland was almost nonexistent and its earlier prominence largely forgotten. The Lavender Pit open-pit copper mine started up in Bisbee in 1950, and soon turquoise from that area found its way to the market, not through active mining efforts but via the lunch pails of Phelps Dodge copper miners who surreptitiously picked up the stone they found in the waste overburden removed from the pit. Bisbee turquoise soon became one of the most popular of all turquoise mines and further diminished the memory of Courtland.

Lionel Herget purchased claims in 1952 and worked the area through the 1970s until his death following a severe beating at his cabin at the mine site, presumably from robbers looking for his hidden turquoise hoard. In the 1980s Pat and Judy Goosherst mined in the area. During the mid-1990s, they made an effort to create Turquoise Mountain Park, but the State of Arizona rejected the proposal.[10] Today the only turquoise to be found is from the old dumps. A legacy endures of Courtland's role in The Great American Turquoise Rush. Adam Herlich deeded the George mine to Gyulo Armeny's heirs in the 1920s and it remained in the family until it was sold in 2007.

Mineral Park

The story of turquoise mining in Mineral Park after The Great American Turquoise Rush closely corresponds to the story of turquoise mining throughout Arizona. John Riggs, stepson of James Haas—the prospector that located the first turquoise claims in the area—identified copper as both the problem and opportunity for turquoise mining. This was certainly the case in the Burro Mountains of New Mexico, and also influenced turquoise mining at Mineral Park and throughout Arizona.

Copper is a commodity. The economic feasibility of mining the metal is dependent on the cost of production relative to the market price. During the early days of large-scale copper mining in the West, copper-rich ore was extracted through deep-shaft mining. As these ore bodies played out and copper prices fluctuated with market cycles, it became necessary to extract the metal from ore containing a much lower percentage, using different extraction techniques. By the early 1950s, open-pit mining was the preferred choice for copper. Phelps Dodge started the Lavender Pit at Bisbee and the open pit at Morenci around that time. The Duval Corporation began open-pit mining at Kingman in 1963.

Open-pit mining requires storing the overburden removed to access the copper ore in huge dump areas. The mining companies had little interest in monetizing the turquoise, perceived as not worth the increased labor expense to sort through the waste rock, and established a practice of leasing out the turquoise concession to remove turquoise from the waste dumps. This provided additional revenue to the company at no added expense and the opportunity for some to establish the foundation for what would make Arizona the largest turquoise producer in the United States.

Leonard W. Hardy moved to Globe, Arizona in 1949 and was working as a butcher and shovel operator at the Castle Dome mine when he spotted an economic opportunity—marketing the turquoise in waste rock to native jewelers. His operation greatly expanded when he successfully bid on the turquoise concessions at Kingman, Castle Dome, and Sleeping Beauty. According to his obituary, by the early 1970s the Hardy Turquoise Company was producing over half the entire world production. Hardy's partner at Kingman, Chuck Colbaugh, split from Hardy and went into business for himself at Kingman. Colbaugh Processing continues as the largest turquoise producer in the United States, under the leadership of Chuck's grandson Marty and his son Josh.

William "Lucky" Brown moved to Arizona from Texas in the late 1930s. After a brief time as a professional baseball player, he went to work as an operator for Phelps Dodge at their Morenci copper mine. According to his son Randy and his wife Nila, his fellow mine workers called him "Lucky" for his ability to win at games of chance. As early as 1936, he began to sell the turquoise he was finding to the Zuni, Navajo, and Santo Domingo Indians. He had a cutting shop in Globe, Arizona where he met B.C. Waddell, who was also cutting there. Brown and his partner J.W. Edgar opened "The Blue Gem" store in Gallup in 1946. They sold both Morenci and Blue Gem turquoise from the mine the Edgar family owned in Nevada. Brown obtained the official contract for the turquoise concession at Morenci in 1953, which he continued to mine until 1984, and also had mines in Colorado and Nevada. Lucky Brown and his wife Bernice opened trading posts throughout New Mexico before finally settling in Safford, Arizona, where Browns Trading Company continues to sell fine turquoise and handcrafted Indian art under the ownership of Randy and Nila Brown.

Today the only remaining turquoise concession in Arizona is at Kingman with the Colbaugh family. The mines at Bisbee, Morenci, Castle Dome, and Sleeping Beauty are all closed, with little prospect of any turquoise ever again coming from those areas. The role trading posts and the Indian traders played in the development of Indian jewelry to the level of fine art and craftsmanship forms the remaining legacies of that period.

In addition to Tanner's Indian Arts and Browns Trading Company, others continue the tradition. In the late 1930s, B.C. Waddell and his wife Jean opened the West Y Trading Post in Gallup, New Mexico. B.C. was active through the 1950s and 1960s mining for turquoise and promoting its use in Indian jewelry. The Waddell family was involved in mines in Arizona and Nevada and became owners of the Lone Mountain mine in Nevada. Today Waddell Trading, under the guidance of B.C. and Jean's son Gene, his wife Ann, and son Mike, continues the tradition and is one of the most respected dealers in fine Native American jewelry in the world.

California

California played a prominent role in The Great American Turquoise Rush. During the following period, Nevada and Colorado became the major producers and California was largely forgotten. Today many are unaware California was once a major source of turquoise, although mining continues there on a very sporadic and low-scale basis. This decline in mining most likely occurred because: (1) much of the best material was mined from 1900 to 1904, the peak years of production; (2) production levels presumably dropped as interest shifted to other areas in response to increased appreciation for matrix turquoise; and (3) in conjunction with the lower-quality turquoise was the availability of new, higher-quality sources in nearby Nevada, whereas in California the Mojave Desert remoteness and lack of water made production and transport economically impractical.

Yet turquoise production never stopped in California and continues today. The Gove mine, also known as the California Gem mine, continued to be mined over the years under different names, including California Blue Gem and, most currently, Mohave Blue Gem. In the old Middle Camp of the Toltec Gem Mining Company, beautiful turquoise from the Riffian Blue continues to be mined. In the old West Camp, the Apache Canyon mine of Ed Nazelrod has been one of the most productive in the state.

Soon after The Great American Turquoise Rush ended in 1910, the production centering on New Mexico shifted to Nevada and Colorado. Tourism brought about new markets for Native American jewelry. The native artists not only appreciated the full range of turquoise color and pattern, but also preferred it. The effort to market matrix turquoise initiated by the Arizona Turquoise Company and the Southwest Turquoise Company met with marginal success in the east coast markets, but found receptive buyers in the West. By 1916, Nevada led in turquoise production with Colorado second. Nevada continued to be the leading producer until the copper mines in Arizona started up in the late 1940s.

In October 1919, the American Gem Company was incorporated, in Los Angeles, California with capital of $25,000, $5 subscribed. The officers, who presumably had each subscribed for $1, were Doc Wilson and H.D. Wilson of San Gabriel, and George S. Madden, F.N.E. Madden, and Dwight M. Madden of Los Angeles. During the next period of turquoise exploration in Nevada, Doc Wilson not only was a leading turquoise miner but also served as a turquoise buyer, purchasing from other mines through the American Gem Company and serving as a source for wholesalers and retailers.

According to C.E. "Ted" Johnson, a key player in the early development of turquoise mining in Nevada, the Gilbert brothers went to Nevada in 1892 and started the Gilbert Consolidated Mining Company. While mining for silver near what is now the ghost town of Gilbert, they found turquoise but were not aware of its value and did nothing with it. Much of the turquoise coming from Nevada during that time went to the William Kley Company in Denver, which had sent William Petry to the Toltec Gem Mining Company in 1898.

In 1927, the Kleys wrote to Fred Gilbert asking for turquoise and, uncertain of the value, he passed the letter on to Ted Johnson, who had been mining turquoise since 1922 at a claim purchased from the Gilberts, the Hidden Treasure. Johnson sold turquoise in Gallup to Ned Kley and to leading traders the Kirk brothers and The Cotton Company. During the depression he sold turquoise to Doc Wilson and the American Gem Company.[11] The leading turquoise operators during the 1920s to the late 1930s were Wilson, Johnson, and Lee Hand. Others who participated in the development of turquoise mining in Nevada included the Edgar brothers—Willis Lemuel and James Welcome. The Edgars moved from Texas to Colorado and were part of the Mormon community in that area. They, and other members of their family, were key players in turquoise production, especially in the northern part of the state.

During The Great American Turquoise Rush, claims were made on locations of prehistoric mines and investors were primarily from the east coast and organized with corporate investment. In contrast, turquoise mining in Nevada developed on an ad hoc basis, with prospectors often searching for gold or silver and making turquoise claims when the opportunity arose. As some claims became profitable, a more concentrated effort to find and develop turquoise mines ensued.

A good example of this is the Hidden Treasure claim the Gilberts first located near their other mining operations in the Monte Cristo Mountains west of Tonopah. According to Morrissey, John B. Gilbert and H.P. Thompson first located the mine in 1897, but could not find a market for the turquoise. In 1907, they leased the claim to H.M. Myers and Charles Bona, who thought it was a silver-lead mine but soon found turquoise. As production ebbed, they gave up the lease, which went back to the sons of John Gilbert—Fred, Herman, and Logan—but they allowed the claim to lapse and it was relocated in 1922 by Emory and Ted Johnson who in turn sold it to the Rocky Mountain Gem Co. of Denver in 1928. During that time, the mine name usually changed with each owner and was known as: Carrie, Hidden Treasure, or the Myers and Bona mine.[12]

Today this claim is known as the Cheyenne and is owned by Jesse Robbins. The difficulty in following the multiple mines and owners in Nevada is demonstrated by Ted Johnson's oral account that he bought it from the Gilbert's in 1922, yet Morrissey has no mention of his ownership. This is an example of a relatively obscure turquoise mine, though it was estimated in 1964 to have yielded in excess of $300,000 over the years. Compare this to the Royal Blue mine. William Petry and W.L. Miller purchased the claim after it had been held in receivership by the county treasurer for back taxes since 1911. Petry and Miller worked the claim for a few years, and then sold it to Bert Kopenhaver and Lee Hand, who had been working the dumps. Kopenhaver sold his half to Charley Bona who in turn sold to Lee Hand. Petry estimated that the mine had been the largest producer in the United States, yielding a value in cut stones of $5MM. This is a bit of a stretch as production from comparable mines during The Great American Turquoise Rush was based upon wholesale returns.

Quickly turning claims, often with a name change with each new owner, was the pattern of turquoise production in Nevada. In the absence of a central corporate structure like we saw during The Great American Turquoise Rush, individual miners, fiercely independent and often thinly capitalized, became the driving force in Nevada turquoise production from the early 1920s to the present day. This model resulted in a proliferation of mining claims, often at the expense of a viable economic model. The miners, including many of the names mentioned earlier, worked independently or in short-term partnership to develop a property and then move on to other opportunities, letting the claim lapse or selling or leasing them to others who repeated the pattern. This has given us a honeycomb of turquoise claims, and even more names, because most mines have changed names several times over the years. These inefficiencies led to a situation of fragmentation in mining efforts that provide little economy of scale and create inefficiencies in production, increased expenses, and reduced profit margins.

The challenges facing today's small-scale turquoise miners have been compounded by strict environmental restrictions that follow a one-size-fits-all regulation that makes it costly and time-consuming for permits to be obtained. Although this structure may not have resulted in the most efficient production, it has spawned hundreds of different turquoise mines, each with their own distinct beauty and personality, making Nevada turquoise among the most desirable in the world.

Colorado

Following The Great American Turquoise Rush, Colorado was second only to Nevada in turquoise production for many years. Harvey and Harvey report that in 1939, Charles King and his family were operating the mines at La Jara at a "nice profit." They employed 12 people, producing between 4,000 and 5,000 carats of "excellent" quality turquoise ranging in size from one to one hundred carats, at a price of 50 cents a carat for higher grade. They also claimed that Native Americans were the largest buyers and preferred more solid colors, whereas the tourist trade demanded larger stones with more detailed matrix. Interestingly, the reason stated for the demand from the tourist trade for more matrix in the turquoise was they believed the matrix was a guarantee of the stone's "genuineness."[13]

In addition to the existing mine in Conejos County, mines were located throughout the state. Near Leadville, in Lake County, two Navajo were said to have located the Turquoise Chief and the Josie May—initially worked in 1935 when over a two-year period a thousand pounds was mined. Wallace C. Burtis first mined for turquoise near Cripple Creek in Teller County in 1939, with most production coming from the Florence mine. Burtis' son Wallace F. continued to work the mine, and turquoise is being mined to this day under the name Burtis Blue. Some of the finest turquoise from Colorado was said to come from the Hall mine near the town of Villa Grove in Saguache County. According to Pearl, this was the first turquoise mine in Colorado to be "opened by white men."[14] As we saw in Chapter One, recent scientific methods indicate that turquoise from Villa Grove had been mined in pre historic times. The Colorado Bureau of Mines states the most extensive period of production was during the mid-1950s. Today not much turquoise is produced in Colorado other than the work at Cripple Creek and King's Manassa.

New Beginnings

The Great American Turquoise Rush covered the period of the largest concerted effort to mine, process, and market turquoise in the history of the United States. As we have seen, no one group dominated this market, though a great amount of turquoise was mined and sold then, as we have seen. The Great American Turquoise Rush ended when demand for Victorian-style jewelry was replaced by new trends in design, popularized in both the jewelry and glass-work of Tiffany and Co. under the leadership of Louis C. Tiffany. A growing tourist market for Native American jewelry crafted with fine turquoise in a range of color and with beautiful matrix design encouraged a new appreciation for the turquoise of the Southwest,

Turquoise was mined in ancient Egypt during the First Dynasty, as early as 5000 B.C. and was considered a sacred stone. According to Pogue, the name they gave was *mafkat*.[15] In China the word for turquoise is *songshi*, which comes from two characters, the first meaning "pine" and the second "stone." Green turquoise is called *lusongshi*. We can easily see the association of earth and sky. In Tibet the word for turquoise is *gyu* and is not derived from either Sanskrit or Chinese, showing that the stone was identified in very ancient times. It is an insult to a Tibetan to call turquoise a stone. According to Laufer, you might hear from a Tibetan the indignant response, "It is not a stone, it is turquoise."[16]

In Persia, where turquoise was probably first mined during the eleventh century, it is called *firoozeh*, which means "successful" or "victorious." The Turkish name is *firuze*. Although it is believed turquoise was known in ancient Greece, the first reference in the West is in Pliny's *Natural History*, published in A.D. 77, in which he calls the stone *callais*.

Our name for turquoise came from the French *pierre turquois* or

"Turkish stone," because it was believed the stone came from Turkey, where the traders importing it from Persia originated. In that respect, turquoise bears another relationship with the Indians of the Americas who carried a name of similar false attribution. During The Great American Turquoise Rush the stone was called turquoise by most associated with mining and production, but was known as turquois in literary circles. Both the Laufer report published in 1913 and the Pogue monograph published in 1915 use the name turquois.

Whatever the name, turquoise has always been a unique gem. At times, it was more highly valued than the esteemed gemstones diamonds, emeralds, and rubies. The Shah controlled the mines in Persia, and kept the finest grade of stones, which he often set in the helmets of his soldiers to ensure victory. When Jean Baptiste Tavernier, a seventeenth-century gem merchant, first brought turquoise to the court of Louis XIII, it was priced at or above other gems.

Turquoise is unique among gemstones. Although others have the amazing qualities of color and brilliance, the finest turquoise possesses a degree of expression, almost a personality, not found in other gems. One beautiful diamond is very much like another beautiful diamond. In contrast, gem-grade turquoise varies by region and even within the same mine. Turquoise is opaque and does not possess the brilliant translucence of other colored gemstones. Instead, it has its own special radiance, referred to as *zat*. Pogue used the term, saying it was indefinable but something like the "water" of a diamond or the "luster" of a pearl. It is this quality that influences the great difference in price between a stabilized turquoise cab, a nice mid-grade cab, and a gem-grade stone. The price rise is geometric—the best gem turquoise sells for hundreds of times the price of the stabilized stone. Turquoise is rare, much rarer than even the other gemstones. The finest turquoise is exceedingly rare, perhaps only 1 percent or less of all true gem-grade turquoise.

The events of The Great American Turquoise Rush are a seminal part of the Southwest and its history. Until now, the details of the period have been related only anecdotally—and not always accurately—or not at all. We credit the characters who lent color and credence to the period and whose lives provided the scope of our narrative. We also presented the context for how turquoise mining and processing developed into the century that followed The Great American Turquoise Rush and into the present in the hope of providing a better understanding and appreciation of that evolution. A review of history reinforces the inherent myth and mystique of turquoise, perpetuated by the confluence of the energy of the sky and the earth coursing through this wondrous creation and exuding a unique beauty, the allure of which continues to this day.

Cerrillos turquoise with diamonds in a gold necklace, bracelet, and pendant designed and crafted by Douglas Magnus, artist, designer, and current owner of the Muñiz (Tiffany) and Castilian turquoise mines in Cerrillos. Photo courtesy of Douglas Magnus and Studio 7 Productions.

Notes

1. Joseph E. Pogue, *Turquois. A Study of Its History, Mineralogy, Geology, Ethnology, Archeology, Mythology, Folklore and Technology,* National Academy of Sciences, vol. xii, third memoir, 1915, 135–136.
2. Henrietta Lidchi, *Surviving Desires,* University of Oklahoma Press, 2015, 57.
3. Jonathon Batkin, *The Native American Curio Trade in New Mexico,* Wheelwright Museum of the American Indian, 2008, 23.
4. Lidchi, 64.
5. Arizona Historical Society, Doty Papers.
6. Colbaugh Processing price data.
7. Homer Milford, "Cultural Resource Study of Turquoise Hill," *Turquoise Mining History Report,* 1994-1, 47–48.
8. Joseph E. Tanner, Oral Record, Cline Library, Northern Arizona University, 1998.
9. Helen M. Smith, "Turquoise," *Arizona Highways,* March 1939, 27.
10. *Arizona Geological Survey,* Turquoise Mountain Park.
11. F. R. Morrissey, "Turquoise Deposits of Nevada," Nevada Bureau of Mines, Report 17, 1968, 9.
12. Mr. and Mrs. James Rose Hardy, "Turquoise Among the Indians and a Colorado Turquoise Mine," *Colorado Magazine,* vol. 15, 1938, 190.
13. Richard M. Pearl, "Gem Mining in Colorado," *Colorado Magazine,* November, 1939, 218.
14. Pogue, 9.
15. Berthold Laufer, "Notes on Turquois in the East," Field Museum of Natural History publication.
16. Anthropological Series, vol. xii, no. 1, 5.

Adair, John. *The Navajo and Pueblo Silversmiths*. Norman: University of Oklahoma Press, 1944.

Anderson, G.B. *History of New Mexico, Its Resources and People,* vol. ii. Los Angeles, CA: Pacific States Publishing, 1907.

Arizona Department of Transportation. *Arizona Highways,* January 1974.

Arizona Department of Transportation. *Arizona Highways,* August 1974.

Arizona Department of Transportation .*Arizona Highways,* March 1975.

Arizona Department of Transportation. *Arizona Highways,* April 1979.

Batkin, Jonathan. *The Native American Curio Trade in New Mexico*. Santa Fe: Wheelwright Museum of the American Indian, 2015, 58.

Baxter, W. "A Bit of Local Color." *High Desert News,* Fall 2011.

Bennet, E. M. *Turquoise and The Indian*. Denver: Sage Books, 1966.

Blake, W.P. "W.P. Blake on the Chalchihuitl of the Mexicans." *American Journal of Science,* vol. 25, 1858.

Blake, W.P. *Aboriginal Turquoise Mining in Arizona and New Mexico*. Read before the Arizona Archeological Association, December 1898.

Blake, W.P. "New Locality of Chalchuite." *American Journal of Science,* vol. 25, 1883.

Branson, Oscar T. *Turquoise. The Gem of the Centuries*. Santa Fe: Treasure Chest Publications, 1975.

"Long Lost Mines of Precious Gems Are Found Again." *The San Francisco Call,* March 18, 1898.

Carter, William B. *Indian Alliances and the Spanish in the Southwest 750-1750*. Norman: University of Oklahoma, Reprint edition, 2012.

Goodman, Linda J. and Levine, Daisy F. "The Mines of the Cerrillos District: Myths and Realities." *El Palacio,* vol. 96, no. 1, 1990.

Haas, J. W. "Mining Reports." *Mining and Scientific Press,* August 23, 1902.

Harbottle, G. and Weigand, P.C. "Turquoise in Pre-Columbian America." *Scientific American,* February 1992.

Harvey, J.R. and Harvey, R. "Turquoise Among the Indians and a Colorado Turquoise Mine." *Colorado Magazine,* vol.15, 1938.

Hidden, W.E. "New Mines of Turquoise in New Mexico." *The Jewelers' Circular,* November 1, 1893.

Higbie, John J. *Turquoise Mining Burro Mountain District Grant County, New Mexico*. Silver City Museum, 1971.

Hill, Gertrude F. *The Use of Turquoise Among the Navajo*. Yselta, TX: Edwin B. Hill, 1939.

Hull, S., Fayek, M., Mathien, F.E., and Roberts, H. "Turquoise trade of the Ancestral Puebloan: Chaco and Beyond." *Journal of Archaelogical Science,* 45, 2014.

International Turquoise Association. *International Turquoise Annual,* vol. 1, 1976.

International Turquoise Association. *International Turquoise Annual,* vol.2, 1977.Jacobson, M.I. "Lippman Tannenbaum: President of the Himalaya Mining Company and a Difficult Person." *Mineral News,* September 2010.

Jameson, W.C. *Pat Garrett: The Man Behind the Badge*. Boulder: Taylor Trade Publishing, 2015.

Jones, F. "Economic Geology of New Mexico." *U. S. Geological Survey,* 1908.

Khazeni, Arash. *Sky Blue Stone:, The Turquoise Trade in World History.* Berkeley and Los Angeles: University of California Press, 2014.

King, J.C.H., Carocci, Max, Cartwright, Caroline, McEwan, Colin, and Stacey, Rebecca. (Eds). *Turquoise in Mexico and North America.* London: Archetype Publications, 2012.

Knaus, Charles L. "Sky Stones." *New Mexico Magazine,* March 1948.

Kunz, George F. *Mineral Resources of the United States, 1883–1884.* Washington, DC: United States Geological Survey, 1890.

Lacy, Ann and Valley-Fox, Anne. (Eds.). *Lost Treasures and Old Mines.* Santa Fe: Sunstone Press, 2011.

Laufer, B. "Notes On Turquois In the East. Field Museum of Natural History Publication." *Anthropological Series,* vol. XII, no. 1, 1913.

Lawson, Jacqueline E. *Cerrillos: Yesterday, Today and Tomorrow.* Santa Fe: Sunstone Press, 1989.

Leonard III, N.N. and Drover, C.E. "Prehistoric Turquoise Mining in the Halloran Springs District, San Bernardino County, California." *Journal of California and Great Basin Anthropology,* vol. 2, 1980.

Lesley, Lewis Burt. (Ed). *Uncle Sam's Camels.* San Marino: Huntington Library Press, 2006.

Lidchi, Henrietta. *Surviving Desires.* Norman: University of Oklahoma Press, 2015.

Lowry, Joe Dan and Lowry, Joe P. *Turquoise. The World Story of a Fascinating Gemstone.* Layton, UT: Gibbs Smith, 2010.

Magnus, Douglas. "Living the Turquoise Trail." *El Palacio,* vol. 119, no. 2, 2014.

Mathien, Frances Joan. "Evidence of Pre-historic Turquoise Mining at Orogrande, Jarilla Mountains, New Mexico." "Of Potts and Rocks." Papers in honor of A. Helen Warren. The Archeological Society of New Mexico, 1995.

McEwan, Colin, Middleton, Andrew, Cartwright, Caroline, and Stacey, Rebecca. *Turquoise Mosaics From Mexico.* Durham: Duke University Press, 2006.

McCraw, Patricia. *Tiffany Blue.* Santa Fe: Lone Butte Press, 2006.

Milford, Homer E. *New Mexico Abandoned Mine Land Bureau, Reports 1994-2 and 1996-1.*

Morrissey, Frank R. "Turquoise Deposits of Nevada." Nevada Bureau of Mines, Report 17,1968.

Murphy, Merrill O. "Turquoise in the Cerrillos Hills." *Lapidary Journal,* no. 14, 1962.

Nazelrod, Ed. "Turquoise—Inside and Out, Part Two." *Lapidary Journal,* January 1985.

Northrop, S.A., Neumann, D. L., and Snow, D. H. *Turquoise.* Santa Fe: Museum of New Mexico Press. Reprinted from *El Palacio,* vol. 79, no. 1, 1973.

Osburn, Annie. *Jewel of the Southwest.* "Turquoise, Bob Brucia's Nevada Gem Collection." El Dorado: Nevada Gem, 2012.

Pearl, R.M. 1939. "Gem Mining in Colorado." *The Colorado Magazine,* November 1939.

Pogue, Joseph Ezekiel. *Turquois. A Study of Its History, Mineralogy, Geology, Ethnology, Archeology, Mythology, Folklore and Technology,* vol. xii. National Academy of Sciences. Third memoir, 1915.

Riggs, John L. *Manuscripts of John L. Riggs, 1924–1925.* Arizona Historical Society.

Rogers, M.J. "Report of an Archeological Reconnaissance in the Mohave Sink Region." *Archeology,* vol.1, No 1. The San Diego Museum, February 1929.

Sassen, R. "The Mines and Minerals of Cochise County Arizona." *Lapidary Journal,* July 1972.

Smith, H.M. "Turquoise." *Arizona Highways.* March 1939.

Snow, C.H. "Turquois in Southwestern New Mexico." *American Journal of Science,* vol. 41, 189.

Spence, Clark C. *British Investments and the American Mining Frontier, 1860–1901.*New York: Rutledge, 2000.

Stacey, Joseph. *Arizona Highways Turquoise Blue Book.* Phoenix: Arizona Department of Transportation, 1975.

Sterrett, D.B., *Mining Resources of the United States*. Washington, DC: United States Geological Survey, 1906, 1908, 1909, 1911.

Vredenburgh, Larry M. *History of Mining in the Halloran Hills, Shadow Mountains, and Silurian Hills*. San Bernardino: San Bernardino Museum, 1996.

Wallace, Susan E. *The Land of the Pueblos*. New York: John B. Alden, 1888. New Edition, Santa Fe: Sunstone Press, 2006.